FIRST CATCH YOUR ELAND

LAURENS VAN DER POST

WILLIAM MORROW AND COMPANY, INC.

NEW YORK   1978

Library of Congress Cataloging in Publication Data

Van der Post, Laurens.
    First catch your eland.

    Includes index.
    1. Cookery, African.   I.   Title.
TX725.A4V33   641.5'96   77-28520
ISBN 0-688-03314-8

Printed in the United States of America.

First Edition

1   2   3   4   5   6   7   8   9   10

In memory of
OUSIE JOHANNA
the great Bantu lady who
presided so well over our
vast kitchen in the Africa
of my childhood that she was
known far and wide as
"Princess of the Pots".

CONTENTS

Acknowledgement

SOME while ago *Time-Life* asked me if I would go back to Russia and write a book about Russian food for a series they were doing on foods of the world. I had hardly said "no" when my right arm and hand, after many years of writing seven days a week, became so painful and worn that a specialist whom I consulted insisted I should rest it for six months at least if I were not to lose the writing use of it altogether. I knew I would have to do something about the desperate sense of being unemployed and unemployable which followed immediately—but what? And suddenly I had a great longing to turn this setback into an opportunity for wandering again all over my native continent of Africa which I had neglected for years. Such an exercise I calculated would take six months at least and would absorb my imagination to such an extent that hopefully my natural compulsion to write would be kept safely in suspension.

Even so, I could not endure the thought of such a wandering without an ultimate writing aim and I wrote to *Time-Life* to ask if they had commissioned someone to do a book about the food of Africa. They wrote back to ask: "But is there such a thing?" Of course there was and to such an extent that my book on African food was chosen by the *New York Times* as the cookery book of the year and is still a world-wide seller. In the course of the journey, however, much more than could be expressed purely in terms of a book on food was evoked in my imagination.

My own family on my mother's side have been in Africa for more than 300 years and there is hardly a part of this immense continent through which I have not travelled. Unavoidably too I have been involved in many dimensions of its accelerating history and the result was that twenty times more was evoked and re-experienced than could go into the making of a book on food. What follows

ix

contains some of that excess, and although food continues to play its evocative role in this experience, anyone who really wants to sample and cook for himself the African way, will have to turn to the *Time-Life* book to learn precisely how to do so. What there is left of sustenance is more of an alchemical kind, which may not be of world-shattering importance but nonetheless has meant so much to me and thousands of others who have tried to serve Africa that I cannot bear to let it go to waste.

Prelude

MY earliest memories of Africa seem to focus round the large dining-table in my grandfather's ample home near the Great River. The scene in this theatre of my past is almost invariably the evening meal. One waited for this meal with the kind of excitement I was to experience later as a dramatic critic before the raising of the curtain on the first night of a new play in London by a friend from whom one expected much. The excitement would start when the coloured maids began to light the heavy oil lamps in the darkening house: first in the long passage which led from the front door on the stoep which surrounded the homestead which my grandfather had designed and built, and last, the largest lamp of all, which hung in the centre of the dining-room. In the middle of this room was the family table made out of African wood so hard and so heavy that a piece would sink like iron if thrown into water. Suspended in massive chains from the ceiling over this table, hung an immense brass lamp that shone like gold. It took one person over an hour to polish it every week and to me it always looked like the kind of oil lamp referred to in some New Testament parable or, better still, a lamp which Solomon might have hung in his first temple in the Promised Land.

I used to watch the lighting of this lamp as one might watch the performing of a miracle. I would experience a great sense of reassurance as I observed the heavy shadows roll back into the darkest recesses of the old Cape-Dutch furniture and saw the lamp-light fall, as in a Rembrandt picture, on the table set and ready for its full complement of guests. At the same time I would become aware of a subtle scent of spice drifting in from the kitchen, despite the solid doors and passage in between.

Scent, of course, is not only biologically the oldest but also the most evocative of all our senses. It goes deeper than conscious thought or organised memory and has a will of its own which human imagination is compelled to obey. Since the scent of cinnamon is the first to present itself to my memory of this moment, nearly seven decades ago, I must accept that my first coherent recollection of the great drama that our evening meal was to us as children, began with the serving of a typical milk food of the interior. I must accept from this also that it was dark and freezing outside because we had these milk soups only in winter. I am all the more certain of this because my grandfather and the African ladies who cooked for him knew that there was nothing that pleased the palates of the young more than this milk soup. It went under the name of snyssels, which means slicelings, in this case slicelings of a home-made pasta, a simple concoction of a finely moulded dough contrived out of the best of wheat flour thoroughly mixed with egg, rolled out as thin as possible on a wooden board and then cut into fine strips. These were thrown into a large cast-iron pot full of boiling milk, already sugared and spiced with sticks of cinnamon. When the slices of this pasta rose to the surface, semi-transparent, the milk food was ready for serving. It would be borne into the dining-room wrapped in its own cloud of aromatic steam, filling the air with that incomparable scent of cinnamon which more than any other spice seemed to us the quintessential emanation of the Far East which had so much to do with our own beginning.

The scent of cinnamon would still be adrift in the room when the more acute smell of cloves announced that the main course was on its way. This was a superbly pot-roasted leg of lamb, studded with cloves from Zanzibar and always so tender that it seemed not to cut so much as to flake at the first touch of my grandfather's carving knife. Mixed with the smell of cloves was that of the saffron rice and raisins, which was not typical of the interior but a taste passed on to us by my French grandmother and which I am certain my grandfather served to us children almost more as part of a ritual of remembrance of all she had meant in his life, than out of his own liking for it as food. With this too came the sharp, fragrance of the quince jelly which was always served with the roasts and which glowed like a Maharaja's ruby in its own crystal bowl, looking as brilliant as it tasted. With it too, seeing that it was winter, went a dish of a dried, spotted bean known as governor's beans, so called because some forgotten governor had planted it in the ample kitchen garden that his masters, the Dutch East India Company, had first made of the Cape of Good Hope. These beans were always cooked in mutton stock and tomato juice and were accompanied by baked pumpkin, flavoured with freshly grated nutmeg.

Last of all came a bowl piled high with yellow peaches. Bottled whole in the summer, rendered a burnished gold by the alchemy of the great lamp, they still glow in my memory like an offering of fruit not from the harsh soil of Africa but from some sheltered grove in the Hesperides.

The meal invariably ended with a reading from the old family Bible or "The Book" as we all called it. For this purpose the table was quickly cleared. The Bible weighed some twenty pounds and one of the most fascinating things for me was that it began not with the Biblical text but with several pages of thick parchment where among the branches of an evergreen tree was written a record of our own personal and private genesis, containing the names of all the direct descendants of the first ancestors to land at the Cape of Good Hope in 1653, implying to my childish mind that we too were part of the greater Genesis which opened The Book itself. The moment the Bible appeared all the servants would enter the room to join in this improvised service.

I would see among them the faces of all the indigenous races of Africa from the tragic one who was the first of all, the Bushman, to his successor, the Hottentot and the dark, tall African Bantu who like us was an intruder in the South and there only by right of brutal conquest, as well as members of the Cape-coloured community—that gay, lovable and vital breed of men, the product of our own miscegenation with the indigenous people of the land as well as with slaves imported from Java and Sumatra by the Dutch East India Company.

I had no means of telling then how deeply this mixed assembly shared in the faith which compelled my grandfather to end every day in this manner. But I am certain from the look in their eyes that they, like me, who at this remote moment knew even less about matters of faith than they did, had a profound feeling of being joined in some sacramental recognition of a common bond between us all. I think it was from this kind of early experience that there grew an unqualified feeling which haunts me to this day. Wherever men, no matter what their colour, creed or race, can be gathered together around a table to break salt as the old saying would have it, they are reaffirming, in the oldest symbolic manner accessible to us, the oneness which life intends us all to have, and are therefore, whether they know it or not, pushed a little nearer towards the condition which the poet Burns promised us with his ringing declaration: "That men the wide world o'er shall brothers be, for a' that."

I have spent a great deal of time with the last vanishing fragments of Stone Age man in Africa, in the heart of Kalahari desert. I made the first systematic exploration of this desert for the British Government after the war. I also undertook a long expedition of my own with the object of trying to save the rare and lovable Stone Age people from extinction. I lived and hunted with them and was thereby enabled to re-experience what food meant to man before he became settled and was still dependent on nature without agriculture.

On days when the temperature was close on 120 in the shade, I would follow the Bushmen across the desert on the spoor of an antelope wounded by one of their poisoned arrows. Once, the pursuit was so long and the need for food so great that the little hunters chased their quarry running full out for just over twelve miles before they caught it and killed it with their spears. One of the first things they did then was to drink the juices contained in the stomach of the antelope as if it were some form of nectar. Out of the context of that day and seen in a civilised setting, this may not strike one as appetising, but for me, one look at the faces of the parched and panting hunters at the time was enough to show how relative to necessity taste was in the beginning and how this sort of enjoyment was, as it were, the aboriginal stock on which all systems of cooking have been grafted and have so successfully grown.

Back in our camp that night I found that the various parts of the buck were all distributed according to the social deserts, age and standing of the group. The liver and the kidneys for instance went automatically to the oldest and most privileged. None of the food was eaten raw but grilled on charcoal made out of fragrant desert wood. Though I could never bring myself to share in what is regarded as the greatest privilege of all—the hunter's reward of a drink from the paunch of the newly killed animal—I frequently shared the food grilled in this manner. There is no meat that I have ever enjoyed more.

What was particularly moving too about eating in this way, under stars so bright and lively that they seemed to crackle like a kind of fire themselves, was the instinctive feeling which assailed me that I was not merely eating for the sake of it but participating in a kind of rudimentary religious feast. My Stone Age companions clearly reacted to the whole process of hunting, the killing of the quarry and the subsequent eating of its flesh at night, in this way. For them food was evidently a great gift of gods and they invariably asked for grace and said thanks for the gift not in words but by song and dance, both before and after eating.

When I asked them the first time: "Why the song and the dance?" the answer came: "We do not know why, except that ever since there have been people like ourselves in the world we have never killed or eaten of such an animal without saying thank-you to it afterwards for giving itself to us for food."

For me personally there was something infinitely reassuring in this experience of eating with archaic man. It revived in me the appreciation and the gratitude we should all feel for what all the cooks in life have done for us, so that I never came out of the desert without feeling the need for a ritualistic celebration of my own. I would arrive out of the blue at a luxury hotel which in those days stood on its own, quite apart from the rest of the world, hard by one of the greatest wonders of the world, the Victoria Falls, or the Smoke that Thunders, as Africans called them.

This hotel used to have one of the best tables in Africa. I would arrive there, not having had a bath for perhaps six months. I would be compelled to begin by having a bath, feeling almost as if it were like the bath of purification the Japanese Samurai had after battle. I would also feel it proper, even though I was alone, to put on a dinner jacket, send for the head waiter, order the best bottle of wine from his cellars and arrange for the most sophisticated dinner in the best sense of the word. Then, at table, with the memory still vivid of the sun and the heat and the dust of the desert and in particular the Stone Age hunters' expressions as they drank their equivalent of nectar, I suspected I had an inkling of what cooking meant or should mean to all of us.

Just as my first memory of Africa comes into focus around food, just as my conscious life begins as it were with the first supper in my grandfather's home, my most recent memory of it too is concerned profoundly with food. Not being allowed to use my right arm for writing for six months gave me a wonderful opportunity to revisit the whole of the Africa which I had explored over fifty years of my most impressionable life and see what the new world of Africa, the so-called emancipated and developing Africa, was achieving on its own now that influence of the European empires had been withdrawn.

I intended, at the end of this journey, to put down in writing my reappraisal of this new emergent Africa. What followed is far too long and complicated for a detailed account. But I can sum it up by saying that everywhere I went I found myself so profoundly depressed that, in an Africa which in its nature was so much at one, human beings seemed to have learned so little from their past and to be involved in more negative and divisive states of conflict than ever before, killing one another from Mali and Nigeria to Zanzibar and the old Congo, on a scale which the reviled imperialists would never have permitted.

I myself worked for the emancipation of Africa and I accept that such divisions may be the necessary price life has to pay before it can accomplish the ultimate unity in which I believe. But this unity, I was certain, could not be helped as far as I was concerned by joining in the various ideological conflicts and differences that were tearing the continent apart.

The great contribution to the regeneration of Africa as I saw it would have to be a profoundly apolitical reassessment of values—a rediscovery of the overriding values of the dignity of man and the reverence for life of which politics could only be a servant and not the initiator and master. The whole level of the political and social scene in Africa seemed to me an eroded and bankrupt one and my whole imagination rebelled against joining in any form of activity in so negative and destructive a dimension. In my desperation, I wondered what all these warring and conflicting systems, countries, tribes and races still had indisputably in common. Surprising as it may seem, the answer that popped up unbidden out of my imagination was food. I thought then that if I did what had never been done before and wrote about the food of Africa as a whole, about African man and his way of eating and cooking from the Stone Age Bushman to the sophisticated gourmet at table in Addis Ababa or Cape Town, I would be doing in a way what my grandfather had done in his home near the Great River when he assembled all the races round the table the last thing every night. Thereby I too, in a small way, would compel a recognition of the fact that in the deeps of life all men in their necessities and searchings are one, and that all which sets them apart, no matter how good the reason produced for it, is evil.

There is a famous Japanese story which the great Zen Buddhist artist, Sengai, illustrated. It is a story of a very simple Japanese woman who wanted to make an offering to her temple. She would have liked it to have been something infinitely precious but she was poor and the only thing that she had of her own was a jar of pickles she had made for her undernourished family. She took this jar of pickles and presented it to the monastery over which Sengai presided with the words: "Please, oh Reverend Master, do not decline this humble offering of pickles because it is all I have." The Master, far from declining the offering, blessed her for it. Like the Japanese woman in this story, this pickle out of my experience of Africa is, for the moment, all that I can offer to the desperate continent of my birth.

CHAPTER ONE

Africa in the Beginning

I BEGIN with Ethiopia. It is the natural way of history to the heart of the matter of this book. Somehow, Ethiopia, from the earliest recorded time, was the magnet which drew such European curiosity as existed to the Africa which lay beyond the monumental world of ancient Egypt. It was always a mystery but a known mystery, made all the more tantalising because some intimations of its reality kept on breaking into the ignorance of the ancient world like those sword-thrusts of lightning from below the horizon which one observes with awe weeks before the great rains break on Ethiopia.

As a boy in the interior of southern Africa, some 3,000 miles away, my imagination was continually drawn to the mystery that Ethiopia remained in my own day almost as much as it was in history. I kept on coming across provocative references to it in all sorts of unexpected ways. I was certain that somehow the market places and bazaars of ancient cities like Thebes, now known as Luxor, and Aswan, standing at the cross-roads of the caravan routes from Alexandria, Tyre, Babylon, to forgotten terminals on the fringes of Africa, must have resounded once with the tales and rumours of all sorts of adventurers and traders in ivory and slaves from the unknown interior.

If this were not so, I could not see how a great and, on the whole, amazingly accurate gossip like Herodotus could give such a precise indication of the origin of the miraculous Nile when he said it had its source in a cloud suspended high over the mountains of Ethiopia. Many years later when I myself stood for the first time at the source of the Blue Nile on the high shore of Lake Tana, I thought Herodotus's remark as good a poetic description of the beginnings of the river as any I have met.

All the books that fascinated me as a boy sooner or later had a reference to Ethiopia. Two of the earliest, Homer's *Illiad* and *Odyssey*, blue-print stores of the Western spirit, seemed indeed to have their whole meaning significantly influenced by the existence of Ethiopia. Take the *Illiad*: in the very first book it is stated that when the fateful quarrel broke out on Olympus among the gods, Zeus himself, who alone could control his Olympian underlings, was away on a visit to the land of the Ethiopians, "famous for their system of justice". Had it not been for this, Homer implies, the whole course of Classical life might have been different.

If I had doubts that the Ethiopia Homer had in mind might merely have been some symbolic representation of what is lost and unknown in the hearts of men, as Plato's Atlantis was, this reference to the Ethiopian system of justice would have removed them. I was to find on my first visit to Selassie's Ethiopia that for centuries it had had a system of justice startlingly unique, just the sort of thing which would have impressed the perceptive and imaginative Greeks. I was to discover that for thousands of years it had been customary in Ethiopia for plaintiff and accused to be shackled together for weeks before they were brought to lawful judgment. It was, of course, a rough justice in a rough age and land, but it always seemed to me to have contained within it the seeds of a really advanced concept, because it sought to compel individuals to accept in the first place responsibility for their grievances against one another and to do everything themselves to contain and resolve their quarrels before society was bothered about them. The average result seems to have borne this out because when the time came for a public hearing of their grievances the plaintiff and accused, perhaps because they were so tired of being shackled to each other, or because they had indeed discovered a way of being reconciled, often appeared before their judges with their problems solved.

The word Ethiopia itself is Greek and means roughly "burnt face". It is another tantalising indication that more might have been known about Ethiopia by the fair-skinned and blue-eyed Greeks than is recorded, and that it was only its inaccessability that prevented it from being better known. The Greeks also spoke of the Ethiopians with an undertone of regret as "the farthest away of all mankind". But even more than these references in Homer and Herodotus to Ethiopia, I was impressed with references in the Bible. Southern Africa, like most of the continent, has always been Old Testament country. In pioneering households such as my own the

Old Testament was read out aloud, verse by verse, to all of us, including the numerous African and coloured servants who were part of our family. I remember clearly how startled I was one evening, not long after I had re-read an abridged version of the *Illiad*, hearing my grandfather cite the gloomy Jeremiah's rhetorical question: "Can the Ethiopian change his skin or the leopard his spots?" For Jeremiah too, apparently, the Ethiopians had "burnt faces".

Hard on this came the discovery that the word *Amhara*, which is the name the then ruling race of Ethiopia gave to itself, is derived from a Hebrew word meaning "mountain people". Amharina words for Hell, Easter, Idol, Purification, alms, and so on, I learnt, are recognisably Hebraic to this day. Most significant of all was the persistent legend that the Queen of Sheba was Ethiopian and the long line of Ethiopian emperors were descendants of a son she had by Solomon.

The Ethiopians reinforced their special identity with this legend to such an extent that the Emperors of Ethiopia always claimed as one of the greatest of their titles: "Conquering Lion of Judah". Ethiopians called themselves "Sabian" people, which again comes from the word "Sabu" meaning Sheba. The Red Sea remains for them the Sabian Sea. So close indeed were their links, in spirit and in fact, with "The Promised Land", that invasions by Babylonians, Assyrians, Greeks, Romans, and the centuries Jews spent in captivity would not break them. Even the most determined and highly organised occupation of Palestine made no difference. For instance, in the time of the abhorred Herod, emissaries of Ethiopia were still coming and going in the Middle East. There is evidence of this in the book of Acts in the New Testament, written immediately after the stoning of St. Stephen. The story is told of how a black eunuch, a high official of Queen Candace of Ethiopia was in Palestine, significantly enough reading Isaiah. He became one of the first converts to the new Christianity. It was this man apparently who on his return to Ethiopia prepared the ground for the conversion of his country, helping to make it, centuries later, the first complete Christian nation in the world. It has always astounded me that so little is made of this authentic episode by historians. Gibbon dismissed the problems of Ethiopia in history with his famous: "The Ethiopians slept for nearly a thousand years forgetful of the world by whom they were forgotten." I think this was a gross, rhetorical over-simplification. Happily the artists and poets of the world never lost touch in their imagination with the mystery of the land. In English poetry alone, from Shakespeare to Keats and Wordsworth, the allusions and images formed around the crude grains of knowledge accessible to them grew like pearls around the impurities within the shell of an oyster. Keats had time in his short life for a vision in which he proclaimed: "I saw parched Abbyssinia rouse and sing."

All in all, this was enough to convince me at an early age that our entire history in southern Africa could have been different had it not been for the long and strangely persistent pull of the known and unknown Ethiopia on the imagination of the Mediterranean world. We knew that our presence in southern Africa was largely a by-product of the search for an alternative route to India and the Far East. But we knew also that this search had been stimulated by a belief that somewhere in Africa there existed a land of great riches called Monomotapo. The imagination of the newly emergent Portuguese power in the fifteenth century was the first to be attracted by the belief in the existence of this kingdom. The thought that, in rounding Africa, they would find a new way to the East was stimulated by a belief that Monomotapo and Ethiopia were one, and that this miraculous land was a Christian country under a Christian king called Prester John, whom they could contact with profit on their way. It was, as we now know, a crazy belief, but it had a profound impact on our history and added to my own youthful conviction that, as far as I was concerned, Africa began with Ethiopia.

I tried hard therefore, as a young man, to go there. Somehow the means and the opportunity evaded me until the outbreak of the last world war. In many ways this delay was providential. Had I gone to Ethiopia earlier I would have had to go in by a contemporary way; by ship to the port of Djibouti on the Red Sea and then by rail to Addis Ababa. Thanks to the war, I was privileged to travel to Ethiopia by one of the earliest routes of history. My point of departure was Rosseires on the Blue Nile, in the Sudan. It could not have been more happily chosen for the purpose of this book. For at Rosseires Mediterranean Africa comes to an abrupt end and the true Africa with which I am concerned begins. The great plain which stretched, flat and bleached all the way to the White Nile and Khartoum lay behind me; the first great cataract in the Blue Nile made further progress by river impossible. The vegetation changed completely and covered the earth with a lushness which, after the desert and scrub which lay behind and to the west, seemed wasteful in the extreme. I am no botanist and I know the trees of Africa only by their southern names but one look at the vegetation around Rosseires made me feel like an exile coming home.

There were the long yellow tassled grasses of Africa, resounding like the strings of Aeolian harps in the evening air, a vast variety of acacia, soaring fever trees, banyan and scrub, zipped with thorn. Above all there was the baobab tree.

The baobab affected me almost more than anything else because here in the far north it proclaimed the oneness of the Africa to which I belong. It is perhaps the strangest tree that nature ever invented. It is a tree not to everyone's liking. Livingstone, in his prosaic manner, said it reminded him of a gigantic carrot planted upside down. For many Africans it is a manifestation of evil. In one of the oldest African stories I know it is said to look as it does because in the beginning the Evil spirit, out of hatred and envy of the Good, deliberately planted it upside down. Even in our own far more desperate and sophisticated day, this negative image of the baobab persists. In Saint-Exupéry's great parable 'Le Petit Prince' it symbolises evil. But to me that morning after eating my last Muslim meal in the soukh of Rosseires and turning my back on that neat little outpost, full of people walking in the heat of the day, like somnambulists, in long white dresses, my eyes fixed on the baobab above all other trees with a delight impossible to describe, because the role it played in my own life and that of the pioneering community to which I belong was far from evil.

We had our own name for the baobab. We called it the "cream of tartar" tree, because from the seeds of its fruit we made a crude kind of baking powder to take the place of yeast. We used the fruit too as people still do in the far west of Africa. Dried, it made a welcome addition to our cooking. On many a hot and rainless day out hunting I had learnt to place baobab seeds underneath my tongue and to let the astringent tartar flavour help keep my thirst away. In Ethiopia, therefore, I taught the men who were with me on my mission this natural device and they took to it gratefully.

On the edge of the town we were in dense bush and at once the insects, the birds and the animals began to appear. The area for which I was aiming was supposed to be riddled with tsetse fly and cursed with sleeping-sickness. We had chosen this way because it was the only country between the Sudan and the escarpments of Ethiopia which was not occupied by the Italians. Since our object was to get behind the Italian lines and make contact with the Ethiopians who had never surrendered to the Latin invaders of their country, this uninhabited, sleeping-sickness land was obviously our safest way.

Accordingly, as the people of the valley of the Nile vanished behind us, the Africa as it was before the coming of man increasingly took over. This was the most exciting moment of the journey: its real beginning in time. I have never been able to play the game of imagining a period of history in which one would rather have lived than the present, for I would not have liked to live in any other age than this dangerous "here and now". But if any other age could have tempted me, it would have been a time which would have allowed me to be the first human being in Africa, and to see it before man spoilt it. Here on this war-time journey, it was as if I had been presented precisely with such a segment of evolution. The slate of the black African earth was suddenly wiped clean of any kindergarten alphabet of man and his tentative writing.

Instead of man, there were, first of all, in the cool of the morning, the doves singing in the same ardent voices from dawn to sunset the same tune they have always sung in my own native south. As the sun rose higher and the day became hotter, they would be joined by a chorus of insects and sun beetles with clear, silver voices. The chorus would quicken with the rising of the sun until at noon, in air running like molten glass over the tranced yellow bush, the day vibrated like a tuning fork with their singing. This hymn to the sun was so passionate and ecstatic that it killed the sound of our footsteps, the muffled padding of our camels and made talking, even to the man just behind one, difficult. Then there were the other birds: whenever one breasted a heave of earth with a view above the bush, one would see them moving over the burning horizon like dense waves of smoke. It was difficult at first to persuade the men that this was not smoke but the shadows of wings. Just as the vegetation which covered the land seemed excessive after the ascetic desert, the life of insects and birds was explosively over-abundant.

The variety was endless. For instance, when one rested in a shade which was not shade so much as a paler form of sunlight, one would see birds hardly bigger than one's thumb busily pecking in the black dust near one's feet, yet bright as jewelled buttons, each of a different colour: sapphire, ruby, topaz, turquoise, jade, opal and amethyst, setting the dust on fire. Through an ascending scale one's eyes were dazzled by an heraldic pageant, from deep-blue hawks, orange and brown falcons, dark brown buzzards to where there hung at the highest diamond point of the day, a lone and gigantic eagle. This brave intruder from some mountain top was the biggest of them all. He poised imperial, so high and so still on his own private thermal current, that he looked like a black spider suspended at the end of his own thread of yellow silk from the quicksilver ceiling of heaven.

Then, of course, there was the quintessential game of Africa: the antelope, the wide-eyed dik-dik, a buck barely the size of a man's hand, the gazelle sprung for speed like a whippet and so on up the scale to the hartebeest. There was a gloss of innocence on all their faces and a freshness as dawn dew because there was no fear of man.

We saw no elephant or lion, but it was plain enough they were there because wherever the track along which we shuffled came out on the open spaces of black cotton soil that appeared every now and then in the bush, the earth was pock-marked by the deep pot-holes made by thousands of elephants who floundered there in the rainy season. These pot-holes were so numerous and so deep that the camel-men had to be constantly on the watch to prevent their charges from stumbling and breaking their legs in them.

When we came to the Dinder river, the last water between us and the Ethiopian escarpment, the first creatures I saw were the great baboons I have known all my life, drinking at the pools. The oldest and wisest of the baboons sat on a blue gleaming rock high above the river bed to make certain that no enemy could fall upon them, vulnerable as they were away from shelter among the trees. They looked so mature and human that I thought of the Stone Age name they bore down in the south: "The people who sit on their heels." Even their language was almost human; as I watched I heard the sage old look-out bark a sharp imperative warning which even I understood. The whole troupe, babies clinging to their mothers' backs, instantly turned and dashed for the nearest trees. I soon saw the reason for the warning. Only a few yards from where the baboons had been drinking, a huge crocodile had surfaced—so expertly that he had caused no ripple. He lay still, stretched out like virgin Moroccan leather as if he had merely come up from the dank mud below to seek some innocent re-tanning in the sun.

As for the lion, we heard him at night to an extent I have never experienced before. In the south he has learnt the value of silence because there men hunt him down without mercy. Here in this northern bush, devoid of men, he seemed still free to command the sounds of night in his own aboriginal and uninhibited voice. There was not a single night in which his voice did not break out again and again in the darkness.

Sitting on my camel or walking at the head of my column at night (because in order to preserve even such heat-hardened animals as the camels of Kordufan from exhaustion we travelled a great deal in the cool of the evening and in the early hours of the night), I would find myself intensely grateful that I was living in a day when such a sound as that lion's roar had not yet vanished from life. For people so shackled with negative aspects of culture and civilisation as we war-time soldiers were, there was in these sounds and sights something of the nature of a prayer for a way of life for sheer living's sake which is Africa's great gift to the modern world. They made the night a temple and I was always struck how, after the roar of one lion, in the pause before another answered it, all the other voices of darkness, like the crickets which raised their own Hallelujahs, would be silenced as if by divine command.

I stress this because it may suggest a picture, accessible to modern man, of what life was before his coming and the long way he has travelled before he could possess the richness of security and taste so taken for granted today. Had my expedition been forced to live off the land, I do not know what we would have done for vegetables, except for the fruit of the baobab tree. The natural vegetation of Africa, like vegetation everywhere else, contains as much poison as it does nourishment and we could obviously not have turned with impunity to what merely looked appetising in that fertile and over-abundant bush. I have often thought that if we had access to a casualty list of all the men who have died in discovering what was poison and what was edible in the vegetable kingdom from the beginning of time, it might exceed the list of men who have perished in wars.

Fortunately, meat was no problem because the animals were still so innocent and abundant that I had only to walk through the long grass for a few hundred yards to shoot game enough for all our needs. Whenever I did so, I was reminded of the world from which we had come by the hungry Muslim camel-men who accompanied us. As I shot, they would run for the animal and quickly cut its throat before it died so that a law of their religion which governs the eating of all meat could be obeyed. It was, I thought, as well to remember that in the beginning the gift of food was sacred. I was startled too because by that time I had become so identified with this virgin land that my own sense of origin had sunk far below the horizon of conscious thought. I would remember then the look of innocence of the animal before the killing and go back to camp with a pronounced sense of guilt. Moving on again in the cool of the evening, as I sat high on my camel, the tall elephant grass brushing my face, I would see the kind of game I had shot, standing in odd bare patches. They made me feel oddly ashamed because they watched us passing by without fear or reproach, and with nothing but wonder in their purple eyes as if we were a welcome variation in their lives.

After some weeks of this, we suddenly came upon man in his first estate. I camped one dawn on the slopes of a strange, large, flat-topped mountain which rose abruptly out of this time-lost plain. One of the characteristics of my military map was that it seemed to be based three-quarters on rumour and intelligent anticipation and only one-quarter on direct observation and fact. It contained such picturesque irrelevancies as that on, say, January 17th, 1911, Colonel X was charged by a black rhinoceros in a certain area, or that an outcrop of white marble was to be found in such and such an area. The mountain, however, was not only marked on it but actually had a name. It was called Dunkwur. It came at us out of the red dawn high above the broken bush like a fortified geological outpost, a replica in miniature of the immense labyrinthine fortress of the mountains of Ethiopia as yet still invisible. I had seen it as a line of blue above the yellow bush at sunrise the day before and had experienced something of the emotion which I am certain made the Old Testament psalmist sing of lifting his eyes to the hills, whence cometh help. The emotion was all the greater because the hill was the first objective confirmation that we were not lost in this overwhelming bush, but truly on course.

We had hardly made camp when out of the bush a small black man appeared, very frightened, judging by the gestures of his hands and the sounds of appeasement that came from his throat. I felt that his fear had been overcome only by some overwhelming necessity. He need not have been afraid, of course, because we were all, from soldiers to camel-men and their senior sheik, delighted to see him. I had my own acute private joy in this meeting; there was both poetry and logic in his appearance. The sense I had had from the moment of leaving Muslim Africa on the Blue Nile that I was not just travelling through the physical world of Africa but through time heightened immeasurably. I looked into the eyes of this man of Dunkwur, knowing as never before that biological beginning and progression would have been meaningless had they not led to the phenomenon of man.

Touching too, was the revelation of the overwhelming necessity which had overcome his fear of strange men. He had come simply to ask for salt. This incident remains one of the key events of the mission. The immediate preoccupations of war certainly remain vivid in my memory—the difficulties of getting the over-loaded camels and supplies safely through that grim, exacting land, the fact that by now the Italians, who knew that a dangerous infiltration was being attempted, had dropped incendiary bombs on the parched bush and started great fires. And yet they never had the importance of this meeting, simply because through this man and his need, my imagination touched the origins of our values. I have never since taken salt for granted. I felt that for the first time I had an inkling of the meaning of that question in the New Testament which like all truly profound questions answers itself by implying a greater question: "If the salt should loose its savour wherewith will ye put it back again?"

The other great revelation of fundamental value from this name-less and vanished man was that the gift of life is always worth the cost, whatever that cost might be.

He and his people lived alone, isolated on this mountain top, because down below the fever and sickness of the bush made human life impossible. They lived by trapping game and extracting food from the bush and the earth. This man's kinsmen brought in later to see us and to collect whatever we could spare from our own shrinking stores bore the signs in their bodies of terrible deprivations and an unimaginable struggle for existence. At this time of year not only had they no salt but no water. They showed me how they obtained the moisture they needed for life by cutting through the end of parasitic creepers which had their claws in the flanks of trees, and then collecting the juice which came drop by drop out of the cuts, into gourds placed on the ground underneath. They explained that they had been afraid because for centuries the only men who came into the bush had been enemies, rapacious ivory poachers and slave traders.

After Dunkwur and another long slow progression through the bush with the ground becoming more broken, and the upheavals in the earth steeper and more pronounced, we came to our first clear stream. Like the discovery of the meaning of salt at Dunkwur this stream too, was an act of revelation in the meaning of water. We acknowledged it by naming it: "Lady Precious Stream", after the name of the play which I had last seen in London. Our camels seemed reluctant to soil so precious a substance. They refused to cross the stream until we had brought up the only mule we had with us—a mule we had christened Prester John. One of my officers, a gallant volunteer from the Royal Household Cavalry, had to ride Prester John across the stream to encourage the camels. Even so I thought for a moment they were going to refuse because the look on their innately sceptical faces as they moved forward, their arrogant Roman noses high in the air, seemed to me as outraged as before. But in the end they followed Prester John, perhaps if only because their built-in pride, which is greater than that of any other animal I know, would have been shamed if they had not done what a mere mule could do.

Soon after, filling the horizon ahead, we saw the great escarpment of Ethiopia itself, a darker blue within the blue, and there began to appear with increasing frequency around us pillars of broken hills, columns of rock and walls of stone, like the ruins of great cities, their roof-tops tumbled in and reduced to boulders. I remember a British soldier who accompanied Napier on his expedition into Ethiopia in 1867, writing home: "They tell me Ethiopia is a table-land. If it is they have turned the table upside down and we are scrambling up and down the legs." Matching my recollections of this homely description with the desolate scene before me, in our last sunset in the low land, I thought I had a fore-taste of what was to come.

On this last lap to the foot of the escarpment we encountered another manifestation of African man. We were all horrified by his condition. He was frightened by such a formidable invasion of armed strangers and was careful to contact us first through his women and children. They came whimpering almost like dogs anxious to appease a terrible master. The need this time was not for salt but for medicine. In this respect they seemed even more afflicted than the people of

Dunkwur. It was significant that the wail of women and children for medicine was preceded by the cry of hakim, which is the Arabic for doctor.

That they were familiar with this Arabic word explained, perhaps as nothing else would have done, the origin of their fear, because right up to our own time this vast area between the high table-land of Ethiopia and the Blue Nile was one of the favourite hunting grounds of Arab slavers. And both Arabs and their degenerate African allies may not only have been the initiators but also certainly the most dedicated specialists the world has ever known in the traffic of slaves.

Yet, in other ways, life here was more advanced than at Dunkwur. These people understood the principles of agriculture. And there was something more interesting and vital still. I woke early on my first morning to hear the unmistakable sound of pipes wailing in the grass. Oddly excited I went towards the sound and soon found a long procession of prancing men and women, with flowers round their necks, following another garlanded man who was playing a replica of the double pipes of Pan, which I had previously only seen depicted on Grecian urns. Man here had chosen to make some sort of a stand against nature; to seek independent command of the means of life. He refused to be perpetually subjugated to the caprice of the seasons. He had chosen his own special favourites from among the abundant offerings of an impartial nature and was trying to cultivate and breed and establish them. Above all, food, salt and water no longer circumscribed his needs and those needs were no longer purely of the body. He sought music and flowers as well for an awakening spirit and was aware of an invisible and imponderable hunger greater even than the hunger for food.

CHAPTER TWO

The Table-Land of Ethiopia

GREAT as the span in time between the two manifestations of man in the sleeping-sickness land below had been, it was nothing compared to what we found on top of the escarpment. How we managed to get the camels up this formidable barrier is not really relevant to the story, much as I would like to tell it. I was supposed to have been met by Ethiopian patriots with mules to take over my loads of supplies and arms, and carry them up over the mountains. There were none, and to this day I do not know who were more surprised: my camels when they found themselves walking suddenly with their aristocratic noses in cloud, or the inhabitants who first saw them. In the shock of our meeting, the men of Ethiopia seemed far more surprised by the camels than the sight of foreigners. Indeed the leader of one group came to me and asked, as if pleading a cause of life and death, whether I would allow him to dart underneath the camel from one side to the other.

"But why?" I asked him, amazed.

"Surely," he answered me gravely, "that would be a most remarkable thing to do."

I still see him balancing himself on his toes, like a runner, at the side of the camel for at least a minute, eyeing the haughty profile of the animal with great suspicion. Then, summoning all his courage, he launched himself at the camel and ducked quickly between its legs. He might have just killed a lion single-handed, so proud was his stance afterwards and so respectful the praise of his followers. It was clearly a brave new world into which we had come when we moved over the last blue rim of rock. Now we were looking deep into the table-land of Ethiopia *proper* and standing with breath-taking suddenness in what was recognisably civilisation as we understood it.

Since the escarpment itself has so much to do with the unique character of this civilisation, it is worth a brief description. Most of Ethiopia lies somewhere between the height of 7,000 and 10,000 feet, though of course there are mountains rising above the plateau to greater heights. There is even one great plateau, the cold, wind-swept and curiously ethereal looking Sembian plateau which achieves a height of 13,000 feet in places. This table-land, eroded by wind and water, has a deep, labyrinthine system of canyons, gorges and river cuts only rivalled by the grand canyons of the United States.

"At one moment," I wrote home during the war, "I seem to be walking scalded in a land of fire and steam well below sea-level, at the next I am combing thunderclouds out of my hair." But taking canyons and table-land as a whole, I expect that Tibet, where the Central Plateau rises to even greater heights, would be the nearest parallel, except that Tibet never found itself in so alien a spiritual and geological context as Ethiopia does. It is true that like Tibet, Ethiopia, even with these immense Byzantine mountains to defend it, might have been overwhelmed by the natural forces of that old, old Africa we had just traversed down below, had it not acquired a very deep-rooted spiritual faith to integrate its inner defences into one determined whole. Even so, the role of the nature of the land in the creation of a unique Ethiopian entity can hardly be over-estimated.

In the months to come I was to travel thousands of miles through Ethiopia. I was to go in and out of it along all sorts of difficult passes and across deserted waste-lands. For instance, I went out of it by way of Eritrea and came back into it through the formidable Tigre. I also went out through Harar down to the coast of the old British Somaliland where the temperature at dawn was 106 degrees, and back the same way. I have been down the escarpment at Mega and crossed the great lava deserts that separate Ethiopia from the Somali Republic and Kenya, I have followed the system of lakes that lie deep down in that great rift in the earth's surface which starts at Lake Baikal in Siberia and continues on through central Asia, the valley of the Dead Sea, the Red Sea itself, Ethiopia, Kenya, and finishes at Lake Tanganyika. But wherever I went, there was this escarpment thrown like a deliberate wall around the land, defending it from natural as well as man-organised invasions.

There was one small incident which illustrated the meaning of time and transition in the condition of man revealed by our war-time journey from the desert to this china-blue rim of Ethiopia. I had with me a young Ethiopian nobleman whom the Emperor had attached to me as an interpreter. As he and I, at the head of the column, came over the edge and saw the first plateau of Ethiopia stretched out before us like burnished gold in the sinking sun, he burst out sobbing and threw himself on the earth crying in Amharina: "My country, oh my wonderful country!" It did not matter that the burly Coldstream Guards sergeant coming up behind us was so embarrassed by the scene that he looked away and called over his shoulder to the officer following him: "He doesn't half carry on sir, doesn't he?" For me, it was another example of how this journey insisted always on bringing one back to the first impact of the first values. I said in the beginning that Africa was Old Testament country. It was, for me, as if I had witnessed the return of another Jacob from exile to his promised land.

All the pioneering travellers and explorers of Ethiopia I had read about, had spoken of it as a barbarous and cruel land. For me, however, the country through which I travelled from now on, the Gojjam, was far from barbaric. The houses, compounds and villages we saw were, it is true, of a primitive and tentative kind. At the same they were of the common bee-hive pattern one encounters all through the authentic Africa with which we are concerned, right down to the Amaxhosa country near the Cape of Good Hope.

The first house I entered stood in a clay compound and I had to stoop to get through the low entrance underneath the thatched roof. When my eyes grew accustomed to the dim light inside I noticed that the roof of the hut was pillared on a tree-trunk. A side of the tree had been hacked out and a clay bed, raised some feet above the floor, had been built into it.

My mind instantly went back to Homer's description of the first night Odysseus spent with Penelope after his return to Ithaca in a room with a great bed also built into a tree. I was not surprised therefore that the first offerings I tasted in this simple setting were truly Homeric. My host was the head of some tukuls, groups of simple and impoverished highlanders, but he made me sit on his only chair—a low crude ox-hide affair—as if it were a throne. His wife then came forward. She came with none of the servility one had observed in the wives of the pagan peoples below the escarpment. She bowed to me with great dignity and without any trace of inferiority. Behind the dark complexion, the features of her "burnt face" were of that most original form of beauty only hinted at occasionally in the faces found in early Byzantine murals, or sketched in the mosaics of Constantine the Great. I remembered this meeting later on when, reading what is left of Amharic literature, I discovered that some of the most moving things ever penned in Ethiopia were composed by women.

The woman seated herself behind her husband and summoned a boy to tell him something in a low, clear voice. Almost immediately the tall young boy, delicately made and in his way as beautiful as my hostess, brought a large earthenware jar. He handed the jar to my hostess who removed its stopper of thick green leaves and poured some of the liquid into the hand of her husband. He tasted it with the air of a gourmet sampling his favourite wine in some fashionable European restaurant and made a face as if it were not good enough to offer a guest. (This was not just good manners but a survival from an age when men did not hesitate to use such occasions for poisoning their enemies and could only prove their good faith as hosts by testing their offering first.)

The young boy then presented us all with earthenware drinking vessels. I was to see far more beautiful vessels made out of silver, the metal bireles of aristocratic homes. These are small decanter-shaped bottles with narrow necks; but for all their beauty they did not make the liquid they contained more evocative than it was to me on this occasion.

It was my first taste of tedj; the mead of the ancient Britons and hydromel of the Greeks. The only thing required to complete the Homeric sense of the occasion would have been a libation poured on to the ground for pagan gods. If Ethiopia had not been a Christian country for so many centuries I am sure that this precisely is what my host would have done.

It was extraordinary how far back in time this Ethiopian hydromel took one's taste. We had come from the parched plain and the thirst and the heat of a long march under an equatorial sun—it was bliss on our tongues. It warmed us through like the finest of wines, but the palate sensed instantly that this ancient, smoke-flavoured mead was far older than wine.

After the tedj came an offering of curds and whey, accompanied with bread made of millet. The bread was served in wicker basket. They were beautifully woven and the wicker-work was illuminated with abstract patterns in colours of a profoundly archaic kind. They

were among the proudest possessions of an Ethiopian housewife and
I was impressed even in the humblest of households by the obvious
care, sense of beauty and feeling which had gone into their making.
The millet bread was round, and resembled thick pancakes rather
than our modern loaves; but it was bread as it was made in the
beginning. It was served with honey which was kept in another
wicker basket covered with a tightly fitting lid to keep the flies
away.

I looked at my own slab of honey in amazement; it had a "burnt
face" too. It was Ethiopian dark and yet so strangely translucent
that it might have been made out of prehistoric amber. I noticed
then that my round of bread was purple. I folded my honey into
it as a miser might fold gold into a napkin before tucking it safely
away. To this day I can recall every nuance of taste of the mead,
the curds and whey, tart and fresh on my tongue and above all the
subtlety of the honey which made my welcome in the humble hut
so royal, and the purple bread that made it so real.

I am certain that my reaction was not due to the fact that I am
incurably romantic about my native continent, for when I came out
of the hut I met one of the officers who had been similarly entertained
in another compound. Although he had been slightly put off
because his host had offered him a slab of honey milky with young
grubs within the comb (because this was one of the delicacies
relished most by the gourmets of Ethiopia and therefore the obvious
due of an honoured guest), he had been entirely won over by the
general experience. He was actually one of the least imaginative
although one of the bravest of the officers. He had often told me that
the kitchens of the world had never produced anything finer than
the roast beef, Yorkshire pudding, potatoes and "two veg" of Great
Britain. He informed me in the Dornford Yates vocabulary to which
he was addicted: "By Jove sir, this seems to be a land of milk and
honey indeed."

There are certain words in the English language which I know
can never be improved upon because they are so completely and
forever everything that they are meant to convey. Among these I
have firmly placed from that day: "milk, bread and honey." In the
three and a half years I spent starved almost to death in a Japanese
prison in Java, it was this first taste of the food of Ethiopia that I
would dream of, partly because milk, bread and honey figured
prominently in the food of my own childhood, but far more, I am

certain, because of the extra dimension their flavour had for me that day beyond the rim of my first Ethiopian escarpment.

These three things became a constant while we were in the Gojjam. Later we were to explore areas too treeless and flowerless for bees to survive. There tedj vanished and thalla, the drink of the very poor, took its place. This was a kind of beer made out of millet, fermented in clay vats by the insertion of an indigenous Ethiopian hop called gesho. I remember in the rainy season lying in Ethiopian huts at night, the compounds outside packed with sheep and goats, mules and oxen and the huts themselves filled with hens, chickens and other livestock, listening to the sound of the high, high rain. My bed was of dried clay with a built-in hump at the end for a permanent pillow. In the lulls between one thunderclap and another I would hear the brew of millet beer in the large clay vat by my head gurgling like a witch's cauldron, and be oddly reassured by the sound. I felt I had come home to Africa.

Tedj is the first alcoholic drink of Classical man. Thalla is the first feeble alcohol of Africa. One encounters it throughout the continent all the way down to the Cape, where it goes under the name of kaffir beer. This word kaffir is in no sense derogatory; kaffir beer is held in high esteem by many Europeans who believe it can cure all sorts of ailments from a businessman's ulcers to a peasant's rheumatism. The name comes from an Arabic word meaning "unbeliever". The Arabs regarded the indigenous peoples of Africa as unbelievers and this was their justification of the terrible sufferings they inflicted on them.

Back in the Gojjam, however, it was tedj that was first offered to us by the heads of the villages. There was hardly a settlement which did not have a copse or at least a single large spreading tree in which their beehives, round and long rather like slender vats or drums of some kind, were hung from leather slings. These trees, dedicated to the bees of the land, were held in almost mystical esteem. I got into serious trouble with a group of villagers because I had to blast one of their oldest and biggest honey trees out of the ground. Our supplies of guns and medicines were running out fast and I had to find a flat piece of earth to make a landing-ground. The only suitable spot had an enormous honey tree standing in the middle of it. It had to come down and when it did, I thought the villagers were going to start their own private vendetta against me.

I thought of Kipling's story about the Picts who went to complain to the legionaries manning the Roman wall in Britain. The centurions had cut down the heather round the wall to increase their field of fire. "You can't go on doing that," the Picts complained, "because you are destroying our bee-pastures and we'll have no honey."

One final word on Ethiopian drinks. My first experience of hospitality in the Gojjam was rounded off with coffee. Ethiopians claim that coffee originated in their country and that it derives its name from a place called Kaffa, where it is grown to this day. Like honey, the taste of their coffee has the same fierce, almost passionate flavour. I remember my excitement when, long before the coffee itself was passed around, I knew it was being brewed from the scent which suddenly began to fall like dew on the twilight air in the hut. I know of no more evocative smell than coffee, unless it is that of bread coming warm out of a brick oven at dawn. Coffee has the scent whose promise is actually greater than its performance, and at its best is an irrefutable and quintessential testimony to culture and civilisation.

We had no sugar in the Gojjam to sweeten the coffee. Since counterpoint in food is as important as in music or poetry I believe that the bitterness of coffee needs its opposite of sweetness to complete it as a truly harmonious drink. For that reason I felt almost ungrateful for the miracle of encountering coffee at all in that remote land, secretly regretting the absence of sugar. I need not have worried because the Ethiopians themselves were instinctively aware of the symmetry taste demands and had long since solved the problem by using honey for sugar.

My next experience of Ethiopian food was of sterner stuff in a sterner setting. The Ethiopian patriot whom I had particularly to contact was a certain formidable Dedjesmatch, an aristrocratic title which means literally "One who in war camps near the door of the Emperor's tent". He was a man who had never surrendered to the Italians. He told me that for nearly twenty years he had never made his bed in the same place twice. He was one of the last few living reminders of how the Amhara have always had to fight desperately to maintain their separate identity in Africa, not only against sustained and powerful emnity from without but also against bitter tyrannies, rivalries and treachery from within. Out of this grew an almost passionate recklessness and disregard of human life as well as an instant suspicion of foreigners and a certain instinctive cunning, hardly surprising considering their terrible history. What is curious is that they have retained qualities of great nobility, tenderness, dignity, good manners and a faith in their own religion. They are paradoxical and contradictory individuals who puzzle outsiders to this day.

These paradoxes go so deep into their character that they affect even their system of cooking, and help to explain their taste for extremes such as, on one hand, the fierce berbere, a red pepper out of which they make a paste served with raw meat, and, on the other the sweetness of their honey. All these paradoxes were present in the personality of the intrepid Dedjesmatch. He came towards me on his horse, swathed from shoulder to stirrup in a white cloak, yellow with dust. His followers were armed with round metal shields studded with spikes. They waved swords and spears as they jogged behind him. Some had slim young pages to carry their swords; others carried flintlocks or guns and carbines of all sorts, held by the barrels across their shoulders. Dedjesmatch himself might have been the re-incarnation of one of the great and terrible figures of Ethiopian history, the Ras Michael who exclaimed: "Safety, where is that to be found? I am obliged to fight for my own life every day."

This first meal I had with this incredible patriot started with tedj. The main course was raw meat. I have never liked any uncooked meat or fish but out of politeness I have often been forced to eat both, as in Japan. On this particular occasion not only politeness and policy but a feeling of imperative necessity persuaded me to join in what is considered one of the greatest of Ethiopian dishes as if I liked it. The raw meat was passed, bleeding and still lukewarm from the living animal, from one guest to another. Each man would take the edge of the meat firmly between his teeth and then, slicing upwards with a sharp knife, would cut off a mouthful for himself—in the process narrowly missing taking the skin off his nose. The few women who were there sat immediately behind the men, and behind them the young boys stood wrapped in their yellow and white shawls, tall and candle-like in the background. The light from the home-made clay oil lamps burning in the compound around us, the torches held high, emphasised the Byzantine in the profiles of their handsome faces. Every now and then our Ethiopian hosts would remember the presence of the women and children, cut off a piece of meat for them in the prescribed manner and pass it over their shoulders. Such a way of eating may sound crude but it is after all not so far removed from meat *à la tartare* which is such a favourite of gourmets in France and Italy.

I tasted berbere for the first time. We dipped our red meat in this red sauce before eating it. If one *has* to eat meat uncooked, it is probably best done this way because the sauce gives the impression of being hot enough to cook the meat. I never grew to like the endless raw meat banquets I had to endure in the months that followed, but the sauce itself quickly became one of my favourites and I always welcomed its presence in the many other Ethiopian dishes where it is an essential ingredient.

Apart from helping me to get over my first banquet of raw meat, berbere was important because it introduced me to the great role spices play in the more complex forms of cooking I was to encounter later on. In this respect, the Ethiopian concept of cooking seemed to me not unrelated to the Indian and Indonesian, and particularly the Javanese forms. There seemed to be some unrecorded historical reason for all this. I imagine that there was far more contact between Ethiopia and India and the Far East than our history books mention. I remember in southern India coming across all sorts of hints that there once had been a considerable trade passing between Cochin, the Malabar coast, the Red Sea and the African interior. It was remarkable therefore how easy on the tongue Ethiopian food was for someone like myself who had already learned to like Indian and Javanese cooking.

Even the Ethiopian concept of bread seemed not far removed from Indian ideas. Like the Indians, they traditionally used neither forks nor spoons for eating but different kinds of bread to dip, always with the right hand, into their many spicy dishes and sauces. There was considerable variety too in the forms of bread available due to the climate and fertile soil which made it possible for the Ethiopians to grow wheat, barley, millet and most important of all, teff. Teff is the finest, subtlest and most delicate member of the millet family. It is made into a batter which is allowed to ferment for anything from three to four days and is then poured on to a flat iron skillet to cook for barely five minutes. The result is called injera.

I first tasted injera when it was warm from the fire and I took to it at once. I can never undestand the disparaging remarks European travellers and visitors to Ethiopia make about injera. Either their palates are most insensitive and unenterprising or, as I suspect, they are merely intolerant of foreign foods. The palate has its own clichés just as much as, if not more than, the other senses. There is John Gunther, for instance, who describes injera as looking "like an old inner tube". Apart from the scorn this implies, it is grossly inaccurate because no tube, however old, could look as punctured as the pale gold injera does. During the process of baking on the skillet the bubbles of fermentation inside break out and leave the surface as pitted as the lunar surface. I think an Ethiopian could counter this remark with greater justification by saying that the average American or British mass-produced sliced loaf not only looks like but tastes like cotton-wool. Even more surprisingly, Dervla Murphy, in one of the most remarkable books ever written about Ethiopia, says it tastes "like foam rubber". This is just not true. It is a subtle and indispensable supplement to the enjoyment of the meal. It generally has a faintly sour, provocative and yet soothing flavour. This flavour makes it the perfect counter to the fiery nature of the complex of spices that go into the making of wat, a rich stew.

Wat is the national dish of Ethiopia as spaghetti is of Italy. Its most delicate and widespread form is chicken wat or doro wat as it is called in Amharina. But of course there is meat wat as well and on the shores of Lake Tana, the source of the Blue Nile, I have also eaten a fish wat. As both chicken and meat are forbidden on the numerous fast days imposed by the Coptic form of Christianity there are also a number of vegetable wats like lentil, bean, pea and perhaps the greatest of all vegetable wats, the complex one called metin shuro, which is made of spices combined with peas, lentils, chick peas, beans, shallots and fresh ginger.

The distinctions between breakfast, lunch and dinner are not as clearly defined or as rigid in Ethiopia as they are in Western countries. In fact the Ethiopian countryman rarely eats two cooked meals a day and often only one, contenting himself in between by munching stale bread, strips of cured meat or a variety of other snacks.

The Ethiopian sets about drying his meat very much as I saw it done in the jungles of Java and Sumatra. He cuts the meat into long strips, rubs it well with salt and black pepper, if he has any, but always and above all with the same red pepper used for berbere. He then hangs up the meat to dry in a clean and cool place for about a fortnight. It will then keep for months, is light, nourishing and easy to carry around and can always be hauled out of store when other forms of food fail.

There are many other substitutes for a fully cooked meal: for instance, the slightly damp and roasted barley flour which one would roll between one's fingers into large pellets, rather as the Tibetans do their tsampa, and then swallow with thalla, if available. Indeed there is the barley itself which one is often given to eat roasted whole. And of course there is almost always, as there is everywhere else in Africa, curds and whey, made not only more tasty but almost unbearably evocative by the subtle flavour of wood smoke which seems to have penetrated deep into their substance. Indeed all my memories of my first meals in Ethiopia are perfumed to such an extent with wood smoke that I find the food cooked in modern kitchens and so deprived of this flavour, not half so good.

When life and supplies allow it, the average Ethiopian household eats its biggest meal sometime towards the evening or, on special occasions, in the middle of the day. There is really no fixed routine. I have had the most substantial wats even for breakfast, and yet ideal breakfast foods do exist. There is always some kind of bread, there are eggs, eaten hard-boiled or sucked raw. There are always curds and whey but above all there are several kinds of porridge. The greatest of these in my view is kinche because it is made out of wheat and not the oats or Indian corn to which the English speaking world is far more accustomed. It is delicious eaten with honey.

Another difficulty in defining the pattern of Ethopian eating is the elaborate system of fasting which the national form of Christianity imposes upon the land. The pattern today of course has blurred and frayed at its city edges, but it is remarkable to what extent it still applies in the countryside. I myself have never encountered a country, Christian, Buddhist, Hindu or pagan where fasting is so complicated, frequent and exacting. Indeed the pattern of fasting was once so notorious beyond the frontiers that the enemies of Ethiopia would repeatedly attack during Lent, because this greatest of all fasts was known to weaken the male population of the land both physically and mentally.

On an average the Ethiopian is expected to fast 165 days of the year, the clergy on at least 250 days of the year. Fasting for the ordinary husbandman meant that he had nothing to eat or drink until midday, though he might have been working hard from sunrise. "After the cock has crowed on Wednesday and Friday," the Amharic book of Observances says, "men may not taste of meat nor butter nor milk nor eggs nor cheese till the cock crows again on the morrow. Nor till the moon on these days may they taste of food and water."

Even after midday, milk, meat, eggs, animal fat and fowl are forbidden so that he must survive on cereals and pulses like lentils and beans. Children are forced to begin some kind of fasting at the age of seven with a rapidly increasing tempo until, from the age of fifteen on, they are made to observe the terrifying eight-week fast of Lent. This system of fasting has had the one advantage that it compelled the Ethiopians to concentrate on the invention of vegetable substitutes for meat as no other culture in the African continent has done. They have for instance a vegetable alecha made of red onions, potatoes, carrots, wild cabbage, green peppers, and in the Tigre and Eritrea where their contacts with the outside world have been more acute and lasting and even their houses are built of stone, they have learned to grow foreign vegetables like tomatoes and to put these in the stews.

The rapid development of modern communications and consequent intermingling of cultures and tastes as well as drastic changes in the government of the country have all had an effect on national eating habits in Ethiopa, but I believe that the traditional ways still have a firm enough grip on the imagination of the people to prevent them vanishing altogether.

On my last visit I found that the scene seemed hardly to have changed at all. The Ethiopian farmer was still there ploughing his rich soil with a wooden plough hitched to sturdy humped-backed oxen, their heads bowed under the yoke, turning over satin furrows in the dark earth as if illustrating a New Testament parable. I still saw the same oxen at harvest time treading out the corn on threshing floors made of a mixture of clay and cow dung. At the end of the day the tall highlanders would toss up the trampled corn with wooden shovels so that the evening breeze could blow away the chaff while their women crowded around with wicker sieves for the final winnowing of the grain.

Down in the valleys and away in the north-east, there are, of course, modern irrigation schemes for planting cotton and citrus fruits, growing sugar and generally speeding up the movement of the country into the modern day. But up on the vast table-land the people still go into their tukuls, their round beehive huts, at the end of the day to a meal where the food is still sweetened with honey. Life and the food that makes it possible and the flowers that make food a delight come out of one of the deepest wells of the past and as such will be worth preserving, as long as there are flowers to cull and bees for making honey.

All this and much more was in the forefront of my mind when I was returning to Addis Ababa from the country on the eve of the Ethiopian Good Friday about eight years ago. The little rains had broken, there were thunder-clouds piled high in the yellow evening sky. The hills were a double blue with the blue of evening and blue of distance allied to darken them as one. Every now and then forked lightning would strike at them, not like the long saracen sword thrusts of electricity one sees elsewhere in Africa but with quick, sharp, vicious kriss-stabs deep into their humps. The thunder didn't rumble so much as ring out, loud and metallic, as if a steel of lightning had clashed on a shield of Olympian metal.

Behind, to the west, down a long, blue and gold vista between two huge temples of cloud, the land fell with breath-taking suddenness into the main gorge of the Blue Nile. Wherever I looked, I saw the highlanders ploughing as I have just described them. But I saw something else: cavalcades of people on horses and mules, their servants and retainers trotting at their sides as they made for the capital to take part in the greatest of all Easter observances. Those who passed near me, men and women, would bow in greeting from their saddles with the greatest of grace and elegance, the women invariably accompanying the bow with a smile that was brilliant on their "burnt" Byzantine faces. The purpose of their journey and the manner of it created a Chaucerian atmosphere as if one were witnessing an Ethiopian Canterbury Tale in the making.

I remembered how, towards the end of the campaign against the Italians, I had witnessed similar scenes and remarked once to a fellow officer that Ethiopia was really Richard II country. As I remembered, the sound of thunder was overlaid by the hysteria of the engines of a great aeroplane and I had to face the reality of what Ethiopia now was—both a Richard II country and a country of the 1970s. But even more remarkable than ploughmen and cavalcades of horsemen with their feudal retainers, were the herds of cattle and sheep being led rather than driven to the capital by tall herds-men wrapped in white shawls. They walked with a long elastic stride, their dulas, long thick sticks which not only looked like but are used like the quarter-staffs of Plantagenet England, carried at the ready across their shoulders. Wherever I gazed there were other flocks and herds moving towards the capital. I understood why the newspapers had been full of prominently displayed instructions and details of the hours and the routes laid down by the authorities for controlling the movements of animals towards the market places of the city. The regulations were so detailed and complex that they might have been designed for an Imperial coronation and perhaps, this is what the ending of the fast after Good Friday is: the coronation of a great hunger. The thought deprived the evening of its sanctity and the scene of its innocence. I marvelled at how all these thousands of animals did not feel the dark, secret intent of their herdsmen but continued to follow them in such perfect trust towards slaughter. It was the most impressive and perhaps the most terrible demonstration one could have of the role fasting continued to play in the life of the country as well as of the fanatical and exacting nature of the fasting itself. It was a frightening demonstration also of what men everywhere are forced to exact from the trusting animal and vegetable kingdoms of the earth for their own survival and a forceful reminder that what they exact is sacred and should never be put to casual, ignoble or wasteful use.

I have another memory that is a private symbol for me of all that Ethiopia has represented. This was a banquet at the Imperial Palace. I was one of some thousand guests summoned for a dinner which was part of the ceremony celebrating the twenty-fifth anniversary of the Emperor's return from exile. The dinner was preceded by a frightening display of fireworks in the Palace Gardens. There is a belief far back in the Ethiopian spirit, as there still is in the minds of men as far apart as the Chinese and the Spaniards, that loud noise and fire will turn evil away. This particular firework display was on such a scale and conducted with such violence that it shattered windows and blew the fuses of the lights in the Palace.

When the dinner came, it was as moving as it was impressive because it was like a sacrament of the history of all that the kings and their captains, who are so fast departing from the scene, have represented in the life of man.

Casting around in my mind for adequate parallels at the time, I could think only of Versailles under *Le Roi Soleil*. There was a footman for every two guests at the table. They stood behind their allotted chairs in tail-coats of bright green velvet, faced with gold brocade, lined with gold braid at the hems and glittering with gold buttons. They wore waistcoats, satin knee breeches and silk stockings, all in white, and black patent leather pumps with silver buckles. They served the food with hands covered by white gloves. In between the sophisticated courses, young men and women, each group in the traditional dress of its province, danced the dances and sang the songs of Ethiopia with an energy that at times was Dionysian. The menu was not long but had been superbly chosen. For every European course there was an Ethiopian course to match it. For every European dish, there was a vintage French wine and the European wine list ended appropriately, in the French manner, with the best of dry Champagnes served last of all and not spoilt as it is invariably in the English speaking-world by appearing at the beginning.

I did not touch a single European dish or even sip the European wine throughout the whole of the long evening. I drank instead the ancient mead, the tedj which had welcomed me at the beginning of my war-time journey. It was a refined and highly civilised liquid with the sparkle of a golden Hock. Instead of French bread I had injera at its subtle best. Instead of *hors d'oeuvres* and roast turkey I had chicken wat and a very special kind of alecha called minchet abesh. This differs from other alechas only in that the meat is more finely ground, and that instead of the usual ginger it is spiced with all the spices of Ethiopia. I could not imagine an occasion on which a comparison between Ethiopian and European, particularly French, cooking could have been more individious. Yet as far as I was concerned, the national food and drink, culminating in coffee from the Emperor's own native province of Harrar, more than held its own. If I had any fears that modernisation would remove from the life of Ethiopia what is good in the Ethiopian concept of cooking they vanished that night at the banquet given by an Emperor who had done so much to unite old and new into a greater whole in his paradoxical and tumultuous land.

The fact that he remained seated at the head of the main table while all his guests rose and departed, as has been the custom in Ethiopia for 3,000 years, took on a new meaning for me. From the steps leading down from the vast banquet hall I looked out into a deep, black sky, brilliant with stars. The Southern Cross was slanted low, the Milky Way was like the foam of midnight sea away on a reef of star-coral. A great red meteorite was falling briefly but with a blaze like a Roman candle towards a night profound as only Africa, great smith of darkness, can forge. And above the chatter of guests and the noise of cars, I heard the howling of the hyenas as they massed in the hills to begin their scavenging in the city.

How soon these lights were to be extinguished, and how near the darkness between twilight and dawn were, in a symbolic sense, I believe only the Emperor, sitting there with a calm as uncompromised as it was impressive, and I had an inkling. It made both that moment and the memory of it today unbearably poignant. I owed this intuition of the profound unease in his spirit and those closest to him, to a long audience I had with him. I had to leave before the rest of our diminishing band of old English officers, and asked for a moment to apologise and to say goodbye. Despite the pressure of the most exacting ceremonial duties, we talked for some two hours.

As always he spoke in that slow, tentative, shorthand French he had learned from a Jesuit tutor when young. Towards the end he reminded me of a night when the two of us had shared a tent in heavy rain, deep within enemy territory in the remote Gojjam province. Did I remember, he asked me, the outline of the principles of future policy he had given me? For example, no policy of revenge against the Italians who had conquered his country, only a new beginning, reconciliation and co-operation. Also, though the League of Nations had failed him and the world, he was convinced that the future could not be faced without an improved model of a world assembly. He would work with all his faith and devotion for some such new instrument of world order and an overall institution for serving the brotherhood of all men. Lastly, he would invest as much as the resources of a poor country allowed him for the education of the youth of Ethiopia. Education would be his main, his own freely-chosen instrument for bringing Ethiopia out of its Richard II state, and transform it into a truly twentieth-century country. Did I remember? Of course, how could I have forgotten so privileged a glimpse into the mind of someone truly great, who had suffered much and suffered unfairly far beyond the normal allotment of mere flesh and blood, and achieved the only triumph worth achieving in life: that of not being soured by his suffering or even tempted to the ultimate surrender of dignity of spirit into sullen desire for revenge? Yes, of course I remembered. But did I remember too how, on the rim of the pass leading down to his capital and his restoration, he kept the imposing array of British and South African staff officers waiting and got off his mule to enter a little wayside Coptic chapel? And did I remember how he threw himself flat on the floor at the foot of the Cross and prayed silently, first out of gratitude and then for help to conduct his life and policies on those principles defined on the night of the plunging rain in the tumbled land, hard by the great Blue Nile gorges? Yes, I remembered all that and more, and especially the tears streaming down his cheeks as he stood up again and walked out of the chapel towards the dusty, winding road he now had to take and said, "*Excusez-nous. Pour le moment nous etions trop émue.*"

Well, for twenty-five years, for a whole generation, he had kept faith with that moment and those principles, as well as one ruler could in a world even less principled than the one that had overthrown him. And the result? He paused, and those dark eyes of his were darker still with their unflinching perception of a new turn of the screw of reality, before he observed that the United Nations had failed in a far subtler way than the League of Nations. It had become the main instrument for defeating the purpose and spirit for which it was created. The education of the young was recoiling against him and undermining all he had tried to do, and could well be the undoing of his country. Only the policy towards the Italians had succeeded beyond his expectations, and that perhaps contained the most important lesson of all. So please, he begged, would I come and see him whenever I could, for he was an increasingly lonely old man and needed the affection and the contact of those who knew and loved him, if he were not to lose, lion heart and all, and fail.

Accordingly I went to see him three times more and each time the mood was more sombre, but the resolution intact and the spirit still unembittered, as I am certain it was even when the men who are now in power and whom he raised in estate, strangled him, shot all his male relations and imprisoned their wives and daughters. Ill, half-famished, stricken in heart as they are, they have to take turns standing in their cells so that others can lie down and sleep, while the men who did all this continue to sit in judgement on others, unchallenged at the United Nations in New York. But all this and more too I know will be rediscovered and remembered when the darkness, of which that last moment at the end of a great banquet was symbolic, is lifted and the new morning comes. He will be there, borne along in some chair of time itself, when those who killed him and so much else are blown away in the red dust of Africa.

CHAPTER THREE

At Home in West Africa

AFTER Ethiopia, the logic of history if not the logic of the earth of Africa itself forces me to turn west rather than south. It is in the west that Europeans began their real exploration of Africa and though the differences between the extremes of Ethiopia and the Cape of Good Hope are real and great, the vast land in between maintains strange similarities of character. Such significant differences as there are exist not in kind so much as in degree. These differences, significantly enough, are not, as one would expect, between north and south as in most other continents but between east and west. Africa, of course, has a geographical centre too but this is humanly, zoologically and botanically so in a restricted sense. Except for a small zone—that is small in the giant measure of Africa—the real line of demarcation is the great Rift Valley. This privileged centre is to me a kind of geological navel, a raw place where Africa severs itself from the umbilical urges and forces that created it. It is an area which, from the air, appears to revolve almost within itself in the pattern of a hurricane, with lakes, like Kivu, of the most wonderful kingfisher blue at its eye, and, at its edges, the last of the great volcanos, breathing fire and smoke over some of the densest and darkest forests of the earth. It is a sort of living museum of Africa's remotest past and of some of the earliest manifestations of life itself. It is charged with the oddities and colourful hangovers of pre-history. It nourishes extremes of mankind from the pygmies of the Ituri forest to the Watussi who can grow to seven and a half feet. It is the home of the gorilla, innocent, gentle and affectionate in his own setting. It is the home too of the hyper-sensitive okapi, a cross in miniature between giraffe and antelope, which, like the gorilla, is found nowhere else. Here also hides a strange, armour-plated ant-eater, who is worshipped by the tribes who live in the forest.

It is almost as if this rift is not just a demarcation line in the earth but also one in the mind of African man himself. To the east of the rift, the land tends to be high and open, bush rather than jungle. The people who inhabit it are in spirit like their native earth. They are primitive in a manly, straightforward, uncomplicated way. (I use the word primitive only because there is no other word to take its place. It implies all that was first in life and has no derogatory connotations. I value the primitive too highly for that. I have always stressed that the balance between the so-called civilised and the so-called primitive in the modern world has never been fairly struck.)

However, east of the rift, from the base of the Ethiopian escarpment down to the Cape, we have, except for a sprinkling of Nilotic and other minor races, the Africa of the Bantu. West of the rift lies the land of the Negro. Both terms, Negro and Bantu, are vast generalisations covering bewildering and enigmatic variations of race.

This Africa of the west unfortunately has no precise political, social or natural frontiers to contain it. In the great nineteenth-century scramble for Africa, frontiers were ignorantly and arbitrarily drawn, dividing peoples of the same races and even clans. Those frontiers are so abritrary that they are constantly being redrawn. In the next century, the map of Africa will be as different as that of Europe from its pre-1914 version. Nor are there any reliable statistics to help one form a definition of its scale and variety. Those available even under the old colonial rule were at best approximate. Now that the cohesive empires have vanished and their legacies are exploding politically like anti-personnel bombs, statistics are even more unhelpful. But some indication of the size is still possible, if one remembers that the old French West Africa alone comprised two million square miles—that is, nearly one-sixth of the whole of the continent. The old French Equatorial Africa was almost as vast and the vanished British West Africa on its own took up half a million square miles, while Zaire, the new name for the old Belgian Congo, part of which is included in my concept of the west, accounted for another million square miles.

Over this vast area the population, as elsewhere in Africa, is thinly spread. It is doubtful whether from the Congo River, up and along to Cape Verde, the extreme western point of Africa, there are eighty million people. Yet the variety is so great that in the

Camaroons alone there are more than two hundred different tribes. In the old French West Africa more than two hundred different languages are spoken. Yet for me there remains an odd basic unity in this diversity which comes in some mysterious way from the earth and persists as a kind of psychological climate, however much social customs and inherited animosities may seek and indeed appear to succeed in denying it. I find this western character more complicated than on the eastern side of the rift. It is still, in the main, what I am forced to call primitive, but in a comparatively sophisticated form. Not for nothing is this the part of Africa where fetishes still grip the imagination of man in such an intricate and secretive manner as to make the witchcraft of the Bantu of the east look painfully naive. It is the land of Voodu, Hoodu, Juju and Mumbo Jumbo. To this day if one travels by boat down the Congo, one can understand why Joseph Conrad had to write of it as "the heart of darkness".

This makes for one of the great paradoxes of Negro Africa. It has a more conscious and highly organised sense of history than the Bantu east, unwritten as it may be. It has a larger educated class, producing writers, singers, dancers, sculptors and painters on a wider scale than in the east. It has an original and impressive tradition of art. The wood carvings and the masks of Nigeria and Gold Coast and, above all, the bronzes of Benin, are as serenely dynamic as any sculpture of ancient Greece. Yet in West Africa one feels that for millions life is still a struggle in the dark with great unexplained urges and profoundly obscure purposes, however bright and quick the instincts of Negro Africa appear to be.

So without statistics or a compass as a guide through Negro Africa, I can map it out only in terms of my experience and suggest an orientation through my own living feeling of the nature of the earth, its peoples, plants and animals. Africa west of the Rift begins for me deep in the Congo Basin, crosses the river into the new states that have issued from the old French West Africa, goes on into the Camaroons and Nigeria and follows what used to be known as the Slave Coast, the White Man's Grave, into the countries which border the Gulf of Guinea like the ancient kingdom of Dahomey, Togo, the Gold Coast, the Ivory Coast, Liberia—the darkest and most disturbing part of the west—Sierra Leone, Guinea and finally sprawling Senegal which surrounds the strange enclaves of Guinea and Gambia. I exclude vast sections of the northern parts of all

territories from Nigeria to Cape Verde because they are so penetrated by the Sahara and are retarded and ragged Muslim outposts
of the Mediterranean north. For the same reason I must exclude
Mauretania, much of Mali, the Sudan and Upper Volta and turn
my back with regret on cities of legend and myth like Timbuctoo,
Ouagadougou, Chad and even Kano in Nigeria where the Muslim
pilgrims come by camel and leave by jet-propelled plane on
pilgrimage to Mecca.

Apart from the character of the earth, one historical factor had
added greatly to the difference between east and west. West Africa
has been in touch with Western man longer than the East. The
Portuguese explorers of Henry the Navigator were already feeling
their way down the coast to Cape Verde in the fifteenth century,
and had even sailed up some of the great rivers of the interior
before the end of the century. The real European invasion of East
Africa started only from the 1880s onwards, with the "Scramble
for Africa". Bad and unscupulous as the scramble may have been
it was of positively virginal purity compared with what happened
in the west because, by the time it happened, European man had
already rejected slavery. From the beginning the west was cruelly
exploited. Along the coastline wherever there was a harbour or a
river inlet, Portuguese, French, Dutch and English came to traffic
in slaves. Most of the Negro population of the United States, the
West Indies, the Caribbean and South America originally came
from here. It is the ancestral country of approximately one-tenth
of the population of the United States. What made this exploitation
all the sadder was that the Africans who understandably knew no
better, joined against their own kinsmen to make some profit for
themselves out of the inhuman traffic. No wonder that for centuries
contact with the West made Negro Africa darker than it need have
been. Even long after slavery was abolished, episodes like the Belgian
opening of the Congo continued to throw a long, dark shadow over
the evolution of Negro man. When the so-called period of cultural
enlightenment set in, even where education in the western sense
was encouraged most as in the old British and French West Africa
(though, heaven knows, the encouragement was inadequate) the
tendency was to run colonies not for their own sakes but for what
could be extracted from them. The result was that Europe not only
taught Negro Africa little that was good but learnt precious little
from it. Nowhere is this more apparent than in the world of food.

It too became part of the rejection of Africa. I have my own vivid recollections of how this rejection worked. I was in the Congo ten days before the Belgian scuttle and the declaration of Independence. I stayed in an hotel called after the Flemish painter Memling who, whatever his other merits, could claim no association with Africa. Like every Belgian house or restaurant I went into, the hotel was air-conditioned. Even the air of Africa was rejected. Everywhere I went I was offered not African food or drink but the wine and dishes served every day in Brussels. An efficient air service supplied the Belgians with produce picked in Belgium in the afternoon and delivered to the Congo the following morning. It was easier to get *escargots Bourgifnons* in Leopoldville than an honest African yam or sweet potato; easier to get a *Nuits St. Georges* than a brew of palm wine or the millet beer which was such a joy in Ethiopia. In the night-clubs one heard not African but inferior white musicians playing the latest European and American hits. It was all due to a kind of nostalgia, of course, but infused with an insolence that was staggering when one considered how minute was the presence of the Belgians and how great and mighty the environment of Africa. It was not surprising that some feeling of guilt and a sense of having taken the wrong road in Africa was always active just below the surface of the European mind. I remember a restaurant on the edge of the Congo near the place where Stanley pitched his first camp. All the people there had been dancing frantically to a frenzied band, saxophones wailing like hungry hyenas, when there came a sudden silence. The silence was hypnotic and for a moment the room was in a trance. The people at table stopped eating, the dancers on the floor stood still, speechless; the musicians sat silent by their instruments, and the waiters poised bewildered in their tracks. A strange shadow of horror fluttered over all the pallid faces. I could not understand it until I realised that another great noise had taken over from the music. What I had thought was silence was merely the mounting murmur of the great river, at that point some two miles wide, plunging towards the rapids nearby. It was the authentic voice of Africa speaking out of the heart of the darkness leaning so heavily against the amber windows of the little club and, for a moment, I, too, was afraid. No wonder the eating, the dancing and music, when resumed, was more demonic than ever. The voice of the river had to be shut out.

There was a similar occasion only a few years ago at the far northern extremity of the west. I was in Dakar, the capital of Senegal. Dakar is a booming, sprawling modern city. I might just as well have been in Mediterranean France but for the Senegalese who crowded the streets and even they made me wonder if they had not ceased to be African and become black Frenchmen. Just as in Leopoldville (now Kinshasa) the food one ate was French: with just this one saving grace—far more authentic African ingredients appeared. One of the most extraordinary sights in Dakar was the magnificent modern market. I found a ring of plump, pink-cheeked French butchers in black and white striped aprons, selling meat prepared in the best Parisian manner. Surrounding them was a wide perimeter of busy Senegalese butchers carving up the meat of animals slaughtered in the Muslim manner.

In the interior it was the same. One hot afternoon I came to a little French inn on the outskirts of a provincial centre some 150 miles from Dakar. I was too late for lunch. All the French people in the inn were sleeping off their meal, but the drowsy French proprietor very kindly offered me a snack which consisted of a bottle of Alsatian wine, a roll of crisp white French bread, delicious and fresh, unsalted Normandy butter from a refrigerator and some dozen different French cheeses. *C'etait magnifigue mais ce n'etait pas la cuisine Africaine!* The pattern of which this is an example applies everywhere in the old French regions and is at its most impressive in Abidjan, the capital of the Ivory Coast where the hotels and restaurants are as good as any on the Riviera. Dining out with French friends, I felt at times I was in the Camargue. However, out in the bush and away from the coast in the home of the average African the story is different. Even meat is a luxury. Sheep, goats and cattle are a form of investment and eggs the small change of the housewife, not likely to be squandered on mere eating.

Fish is more common and abundant. Along coast and river it is available fresh, in the bush and country in between it is salted and dried. The African smallholder, and even the richer peasants are forced to live, if lucky enough to have goats and cattle, on milk, curds and whey, vegetables, pulses and cereals. Even for these the nature of the land and the inadequate husbandry imposes a system of rationing, and they are compelled to turn for bulk in their nourishment to farinacious tubers like manioc or kassawa, yams and sweet potatoes.

Even so the ingenuity of the countryman in drawing on the

plants of plain and forest is impressive; the long, inarticulate years of his existence in Africa have taught him what is most nutritious. Our old friend the baobab, for instance, is plundered for its fruit. The seeds are dried, crushed and ground and used for flavouring in stews. The flesh is dried and stamped into a fine powder and used to thicken sauces and gravies, adding a subtle tart flavour of its own. There are, in each locality, numerous forest fruits and leaves that have no European or American equivalent. There is no point, therefore in cataloguing them, though it is a pity because they are essential to African food. It is often impossible even to establish their botanical names. I have learned in my travels through Africa that geological information is easy to come by but botanical material, difficult or impossible. The European knew all about Africa's rocks because his over-riding interest was in the mineral wealth of the land. His interest in plants was marginal and for centuries, with rare exceptions, hardly stretched beyond what was necessary for his own nourishment. Even where he did turn to the land he did so again for profit and encouraged the indigenous peoples to develop an economy aimed more at producing wealth than a balanced diet. Hence that sinister phrase still current in English-speaking Africa: "Cash crops".

For the same motives the French, with their sense of rational logic, subjected their part of Africa to similarly unhelpful systems of agricultural planning. They divided it into vast zones. Senegal, for example, was reserved exclusively for peanuts, other areas for cotton, sisal, palm oils, cocoa and so on with the result that one of the greatest battles of the new Africa is to create a truly diversified economy. In what was Portuguese Africa and to a certain extent in East Africa the story is rather different and we shall come to it later. But the truth remains that the majority of the peoples of West Africa still do not live so much as subsist. However great their inborn talent for cooking and the ingenuity displayed in making the most of slender resources, there is little to be learned from them in this regard.

The contrast between life in towns and in the bush is therefore bewildering. This is particularly true of ex-French Africa, if only because the French attach so much more importance to food and spend so much more money on it. Not long ago I accompanied a charming young Frenchman, whose family have a timber concession in the far interior of the Ivory Coast, through what is potentially one of the richest parts of French Africa. We went by jeep through hundreds of miles of dense jungle to his headquarters, where we lived and ate as we might have done in provincial France. What was so significant about our journey was the fact that everyone in the land could have lived and eaten as well. The land is singularly blessed with rivers, fertile soils and hills and provides variations of climate and earth which, with imagination, could have been made to grow almost every conceivable vegetable and plant. If only the Europeans had applied themselves to this aspect of life in Africa earlier, the West African's diet would have been as rich and varied as theirs. No doubt this will come about. In a way it has already started to happen.

The great Empires, in a belated change of values during the last few years of their Imperial term, paid more attention to these matters. The results of all they learned from the experimental institutions and farms they created are penetrating into the interior and are slowly being disseminated throughout the land.

Signs of this were apparent in the country my French friend and I visited round about his Ivory Coast concession. Many villages were still built of wood, clay, dung and thatch in the pattern common to all Africa. Families still huddled around a common iron pot, eating their bean and yam stew with their hands in a smoke-filled atmosphere as they have done for a thousand years. Yet we did find evidence of change. One night heavy rain made us take shelter with a lonely peasant. He tilled a broad spit of fertile earth between the bush and a wide river. Instead of yams, kassawa and sweet potatoes, he was growing rice. His two wives kept hens and Muscovy ducks. He also kept goats, and fished successfully in the river with round wicker traps, broad at the mouth and shaped like a funnel within a funnel. He seemed to me one of the most contented people I had ever met and his sense of hospitality was great. We sat down to dinner on mats woven of river rushes, eating food served on wooden platters. For an *hors d'oeuvres* we had a four-gallon paraffin tin full of forest snails. These snails are a feature of the West African tropical and sub-tropical world. One sees them in markets everywhere and in the cities the competition to buy them is keen. The Ivory Coast variety reminded me very much of the snails one finds in the Gloucestershire woods (where they are called Roman snails to this day, after the invaders who introduced them into the country). Our African host threw the snails live on to charcoal and after roasting them briefly piled them onto a platter. We quickly learned to extract their meat with wooden pins. A vessel containing a sauce made of palm oil, chopped wild parsley and crushed pepper and salt, was continually passed round. Snails are not my favourite food but so much trouble had gone into their collection and preparation and they were so obviously a luxury to our host that I had to pretend to enjoy them.

For a main course, he had killed some of his wives' precious chickens, grilled them on coals of aromatic wood and served them with his home-grown and roughly husked rice. The cooked rice had a reddish tinge to it, rather like the unpolished rice the Japanese serve to brides and bridegrooms at the final marriage ceremony, as an aid to virility. We drank a fiery palm wine. Finally, some bottles of coca-cola were proudly produced but both my French companion and I refused them. We realised that accepting them, even in a household so advanced by African standards, would have been like extracting champagne from a peasant in Europe. Somehow, these bottles were evidence, even more startling than the cultivation of rice, of the ferment which will continue to transform Africa.

In the old British Africa the picture was slightly more encouraging. All the Latin countries treated their African colonies as integral departments of their metropolitan areas. The British, for all their faults, believed in something they called indirect rule, which respected the identity of indigenous Africa and encouraged it to develop in terms of its own traditions. The result is that indigenous customs there, even in this emancipated day, are far more vigorous than in other parts of the west. The Yoruba of Nigeria and the Ghanaians of the Gold Coast, to mention only two, still observe rituals that are deeply rooted products of their history. Moreover, the British missionaries, for all their restricted outlook in other ways, seem to have had the same sort of approach as their political counterparts. However much the British may have stuck to gin-slings and whisky, roast beef and Yorkshire puddings in their own clubs and homes, they had some inkling of the importance of encouraging the Africans to make the best use of their own raw materials. Once there was not a city or town of any importance in the old British Africa which was without a mission book-shop containing cookery books written by missionary ladies for the guidance of African housewives. These cookery books still make touching reading because they are a mixture of the author's nostalgia for their own native foods and their desire to give Africans a more balanced diet. Their emphasis, however, was obviously not on taste so much as on the health of the consumer.

The authors all clearly recognised that the battle in the African kitchen was against the excess of starch in the diet. I think of it as the battle against the yam, a battle which is still being fought in Africa because the average man's diet remains singularly poor in proteins. All along the west coast of Africa, the yam is not just an ingredient for food but part of the emotions of people. These emotions are even stronger than those the Irish feel for the potato. The truth is that, for all its deficiencies, the yam enabled the West African to survive. His gratitude to the yam accordingly is so great that eating it is almost a religious exercise. Yam feast-days are still common in West Africa. They are seen at their best in Ghana where yam dishes are brought into the ceremonies that accompany birth, marriage, recovery from accidents or ill-health and the overcoming of sorrow after death. On these occasions the Ghanaian will eat his yam in one of many ingenious ways, often accompanied by eggs, because the egg for him is a symbol of fertility. There is an old African saying which might well have originated in Ghana: "The sun too is but an egg which hatches great things." Even at the great Ghanaian festival called "Hooting at Hunger", celebrated with the most colourful costume and pageantry at the beginning of the African autumn (a kind of pagan equivalent of Harvest Festival), the yam holds its own in spite of the fact that it has a strong rival in krekple, a dish which is prepared from maize flour and eaten with a brew of fish and palm-nut oil. There is not only gratitude but poetic justice in this, because maize, however loved and widely spread in Africa today, is a foreigner; the yam is a native of the land.

Another outsider, a sort of first-line reinforcement of the yam in the battle against hunger in West Africa, is manioc or kassawa. It goes by a multitude of names according to the locality in which it is found; generically it is the tuber from whose flour tapioca is made. Its leaves are used in many ways in West African cooking but it is the tuber's flour which is used to give bulk to the meagre West African diet. The cooking of this tuber is by no means simple because, like many tubers, the skin contains poison—even the skin of the potato can be slightly toxic. The form in which kassawa is considered most delectable is a fermented one, known as garri. One has only to mention garri to a Ghanaian abroad to produce an immediate attack of home-sickness.

In West Africa, the best meals I have eaten have been in the homes of the new middle classes. Only a few years ago, on a long journey that included the whole of Africa south of the Sahara, I found myself driven from the hotels and restaurants of the cities to the tables of my African friends, like a refugee fleeing from a totalitarian terror. I could not have done so a decade ago. I have never realised so clearly as on this journey, made so soon after travelling in Russia, the Far East, Western Europe and North America, how our taste in food is increasingly threatened by the dictatorship of an expanding international cuisine. This tyranny has its agents in the modern hotels and restaurants everywhere. Their chefs and managers, drawn mostly from the Western world, are its gestapo and the *maitres d'hôtels* of the restaurants, whether they cook and brew under Italian, French, German, Swiss or other labels, are increasingly a species of gastronomic gauleiter compelling permissive palates to endure food of a uniformly colourless savour.

The palate of Western man is in any case over-indulged and jaded. Everything has become too easy for him. He has succeeded in eliminating the seasons in cooking. Only those who grew up in pioneering communities, as I did, can remember how much the joy of eating owes to the discipline of the seasons. We all tend more and more to eat as if life were just one long summer. But in the homes of these West African friends of mine cooking, after thousands of years of deprivation, is still a discovery. Their approach has a kind of morning freshness about it; their taste is exhilaratingly exploratory and the housewives' invention active and fertile. Their meals stimulate not only the palate but also the mind, and some of the best conversations I have ever heard have taken place over food eaten with African friends.

I found it reassuring for the future of cooking in Africa that its main impulses come from these rapidly expanding middle classes because great as the contributions of the peasant and aristocrat may have been to the art of cooking in the beginning, the middle classes have always been the real consolidators and developers of taste in the post-Renaissance world. It is no accident that one can eat no better in France than *à la Bourgeoisie*.

As an example of this inventive spirit it is worth looking at what can be done with the basic yam. The commonest method of cooking yams is to boil them and, after boiling, to peel them and cut them into slices or mash them and serve them as a purée. But on the sophisticated West African table of today I have had them served with grilled chicken or fish as delicious croquettes, par-boiled and then browned in palm or ground-nut oil. I have had them *à la Dauphine* or as a sort of *pomme Lyonnais*, cooked in layers with finely sliced onions, grated cheese and bread-crumbs. I have eaten them baked, sweetened with dark black sugar and sticks of cinnamon, as an accompaniment to the rare cut of venison which one still gets in the interior.

Palm-nut oil has become an essential of West African cooking and provides the most characteristic ingredient—indeed one really cannot know what the authentic dishes should taste like unless they have been prepared with it. After palm-nut oil, the oil extracted from the peanut is the nearest favourite, although the peanut has the additional virtue of being eaten for its own sake as well. The Western world already knows the salted peanut and the so-called peanut butter that is made from it, but these are really only two of its elementary forms. One of its most common uses in Africa is as the main ingredient of many different sauces.

Important as it is as an accompaniment to other substances, the peanut plays a considerable role in puddings, tarts, cakes, maca-roons and biscuits. But for me the ultimate consummation of the peanut is in the cold season. With the heavy rain falling and the thunder resounding outside, I love it best of all as a good wholesome soup, welcome and warming as potage paysanne in the Ardennes on a cold winter's night.

Almost as important as peanuts and palm oil both in the economy and the cooking of West Africa is, of course, the coconut. Its uses are not perhaps quite as basic as those of the others but they are nonetheless varied and numerous. I have eaten coconuts in Dahomey, for instance, in the home of a fellow African writer where a chicken, roasted and flavoured with onions, pimento, turmeric and a clove of garlic was served with boiled rice and a sauce made out of the pulp of coconuts cooked in their own milk plus a little hot water. This sauce was an integral part of the chicken dish because it was poured into the roasting pot for the last fifteen minutes of cooking. The chicken was frequently basted with it, and when it appeared on the table the chicken, the sauce and other spices were therefore completely at one. This sauce, in particular, always seemed to me to be one of the better liaison agents between plain boiled rice and roasted chicken.

Coconut milk is used directly in cooking rice and the two go happily together; the milk incidentally is not the water inside the coconut but the liquid extracted from its flesh. Both in Nigeria and Ghana I have eaten coconut rice as a delicious accompaniment to shellfish of all kinds. From Cape Verde to Zaire either the milk or the flesh of the coconut, or both pulped together, are used to produce original variations of taste and savour to all sorts of soups, stews and roasts, both of fish and meat. The best frejons of Nigeria, the endless purées they make out of their many varieties of indigenous beans, would be unthinkable without coconut milk, particularly on Good Friday, when sugar is added and it is eaten as a pudding by itself.

One outstanding characteristic of West African cooking is that fish and meat are very often cooked together. This of course is quite common in Portugal and to some extent in Spain. Whether Portugal brought the idea to Africa, or Africa gave it to Portugal, is immaterial. One method is for the meat to be diced and added to smoked or salted fish, which has been flaked and boned. Both are browned in palm oil before being mixed with chopped yam, onions, tomatoes, diced pimentos, herbs and the whole simmered in a mixture of oil and water. When the meat is tender, the dish is ready.

The sea and rivers of West Africa are singularly blessed with fish, a source of food which, though tapped from the earliest days, has never been fully exploited and whose great potential is only just beginning to be recognised. A sign of the times on my last journey through West Africa was that, in the decade which had passed since my previous visit, I found fish barbecues a growing fashion among my friends. Beef and mutton in West Africa is not merely scarce but, when available, seems to have come from animals trained all their lives as long distance runners. In this regard, it could be said of the West African cook that his problem is how to make good use of bad material. One thinks of the old generalisation that French cooking was so good precisely because it made indifferent material delicious, while in Great Britain first class material was transformed into something almost inedible. In this respect the West African cook resembles the French rather than the British.

Even the chicken, the favourite delicacy of the West African table, is rarely tender enough for roasting or grilling straight away

but has to be marinated not for flavour so much as to make it tender enough for real enjoyment. This problem does not arise with fish. West African fish moreover tend to be fleshier and more substantial than those caught in European waters. They therefore lend themselves more readily to grilling or roasting in the open. I have many pleasant recollections of sitting by a fire in the soft West African night, watching my hostess roast a fifteen pound fish on charcoal, my appetite increasing as the smell of wood smoke, fish and the palm oil used for basting grew denser.

All households had their own way of preparing the oil used in barbecues. It was usually spiced with crushed herbs, pimentos, onions and garlic, but combinations and additions varied from one home to another. The fish usually had deep incisions which looked like the local tribal pattern in the glow of the fire. From time to time the spiced oil was ladled over the fish while a metal scoop with a long handle was held underneath the grill so that most of the juices released by the basting could be gathered and set aside for making a fine hot natural sauce to serve with the rice or yam purée which went with the fish.

Perhaps the greatest natural experts in cooking fish in this manner were the tribes who inhabit the upper reaches of the Congo River whose main diet it is. The physical stature of both men and women and their vigour and intelligence is in itself, a testimony to such a diet. The skill with which they build their traps, the courage they display in fishing in the most dangerous rapids, where, as all good African fishermen know, the biggest and most succulent of fish gather, is most impressive. I have been with them when they have caught tiger fish and perch that must have weighed anything between fifteen and thirty pounds and eaten them fresh, grilled then and there. Away from their villages, they cooked their catch on improvised spits made out of green lathes cut from the trees in the surrounding jungle. They latticed them into a grille which they suspended over the charcoal, the ends resting in the forks of upright sticks pressed firmly into the ground at the sides of the fire. The lathes were sappy and green enough not to burn but would emit a smoky vapour that added flavour to the fish.

I remember one meal with Senegalese friends which is worth examining in detail because it illustrates in miniature the evolution of cooking in Africa as well as the particular dishes themselves.

The meal started with a sort of Senegalese quiche. The pastry was remarkable because of its extremely light and thin texture. The filling was a very finely flaked smoked fish to which had been added chopped onions, ground grilled peanuts, diced pimento and fresh tomato purée, all well mixed together. A whisked egg was folded in at the last minute and the whole baked in a very hot oven for about twenty minutes.

The main dish, however, was chicken yassa. The plucked and dressed chicken had been boned and jointed rather as a Chinese cook might have done. Then, since even the best roasting chickens in Africa seem to have graduated as marathon runners, the fillets had been thoroughly beaten with a rolling pin to make them more tender. My hostess told me that very often in the cool season the fillets are tightly wrapped in pawpaw leaves and left in a cool place overnight because that helps to make them not only more tender but gives them a more subtle flavour. On this occasion, however, she had transferred the chicken straight from the pounding board into a marinade of lemons, onions, pimentos and peppers. It had been left for only half an hour and then grilled until crisp and brown. While the grilling went on, she had extracted the onions from the marinade and browned them separately in palm oil before placing them in a casserole with the marinade and the chicken, which was allowed to simmer for a quarter of an hour. (She told me she used exactly the same method for mutton cutlets, steaks and fish.) The chicken was served with a dish of white boiled rice. The meal ended with a fruit salad of very finely sliced banana, diced fresh pineapples and guavas. The pineapple casing had been hollowed out and each of us had half a casing filled with salad, and a very cold custard flavoured with vanilla pods was served.

I have left for the last one of my favourite dishes. It is called rice joloff. It is made either with chicken or meat or with both combined. The dish is native to Nigeria but it has spread all over the old British West Africa and is so firmly established that it appears quite naturally in many homes on Sundays at the head of the table. Even the hotels and restaurants, despite their international prejudices, now happily include it in their menus.

My most recent memory of joloff rice was eating it in a small restaurant on a spit of sand that bars the long Atlantic swell from breaking into Freetown harbour. I remember it vividly because the whole of the new Africa seemed to come to a point in the occasion. I had been strongly urged by my African friends not to venture so far out of the city at night because the country, like almost every part of the West Africa through which I had travelled, was in a turmoil which at times assumed dangerous forms. I had already arrived, some ten days previously, in Bamako in Mali, only to find the place in a state of revolution. I was not allowed to leave the airport and had to fly on to Conakry within a few hours of my arrival. In Freetown itself on the day of my arrival some demonstrator was shot dead in a street within a few yards of me and almost on the steps of my hotel a European visitor, returning late at night, had been cruelly savaged by some thugs. The privileged Creole population of the coast and the tribes within the interior who have never liked one another seemed ready to fly at one another's throats.

However, I arrived at my destination without mishap just as the sun was going down. It was the kind of sunset one seems to get only in Africa. The scarlet sun on the edge of a purple sea seemed three times its normal size and, as always in the tropics, in a hurry to sink. Indeed it seemed to plunge into the sea with such speed and violence that the immense thunder-clouds piled high in a turquoise-blue sky appeared to be caught up into a kind of whirlpool of valedictory light and to be sucked after the foundering sun like flotsam and jetsam of the air. There was an odd sort of mythology in it all, a strange, pronounced kind of *Götterdämmerung* feeling. The lovely green mountains in the interior were quickly lost in darkness before becoming festooned with garlands of electric light. Hard by the little restaurant where we sat down to eat under a fringe of palms, lay the large, pretentious yacht of the President of the desperately impoverished Liberia which had run aground during a state visit of pomp and flabby splendour. The ship was relatively undamaged, but no attempt appeared to have been made to salvage it. In that situation it, too, added to the feeling of disaster induced by the swift going down of the sun. Beyond the wreck stood a kind of casino where diamond miners and smugglers from the interior came to gamble away their money. On a hill near the casino stood a very large concrete hotel on which building had stopped some three years before and, one was told, would never be resumed. On one side of the land lay the smooth black waters of the harbour, a lagoon of reflected light; on the other side the long Atlantic rollers, with no land between Freetown and Brazil to impede their rhythm, made music. Whenever the foaming surf retreated, to be resurrected in another great comber, it left the sands shining like a mirror. Yet when the night was once firmly established, the sense of resolution was complete. There is no land in the world which so quickly forgets the sun and takes so happily to the night as this dark land of West Africa.

At my table the smell of the sea and the warm breath of grass and jungle on a terrace under palms evoked Africa at its best. My imagination was quickened with intimations of the wonder that could still be worked in so relatively untouched and so beautiful a setting with such fresh and responsive human material. The quickening was all the keener because it was my last night in Africa and I knew that in less than twenty-four hours I would be back again in the teeming, pre-conditioned world of London.

I felt an extra compulsion to see that I had nothing but African food, so, as a ritual of farewell, I began with a large avocado pear which was filled with flaked and delicately smoked West African fish, covered with a sauce made out of purely African material. The West African waiter, dignified and impeccable as a royal steward, told me that the sauce was made out of the yokes of hard-boiled eggs, passed through the finest of sieves to be stirred up vigorously with a little milk until they were of a smooth mayonnaise consistency. Some lemon juice and some ground nut oil, a little sugar, just enough to appease the lemon, and some grated nutmeg was stirred into the sauce which was then poured over the flaked fish. The stuffing was criss-crossed on top with the finest of sliced pimentos. It made so good an *hors d'oeuvres* that I had two helpings. For a main dish I had joloff rice, made with chicken and with large slices of pumpkin. The pumpkin had been dusted with dark brown sugar, some cinnamon and baked in the oven with palm oil. Just before serving, some drops of fresh lime were squeezed on to the pumpkin.

I ended with a pineapple fritter. When I saw the name fritter on the menu, I recoiled because nobody can move about the English-speaking world as much as I do and not live in some terror of this kitchen cliché. But the head-waiter insisted that on such a night I could do no better and as all the other substitutes on the menu were international I submitted to his advice.

A large party of Russians and I were the only Europeans in the restaurant, all the rest of the diners were West Africans. I had felt a glutton ordering my *hors d'oeuvres* twice but I felt less greedy when I saw the Russians asking for repeats of every course twice and some even three times. It did not surprise me because I had seldom eaten as well as in Russia. In particular I was not surprised how they clamoured again and again for the pineapple fritters.

Not many years before, travelling in the Trans-Siberian railway, I stopped at a far-Eastern station. A rumour went round instantly, like news of a declaration of war, that the dining-car had some bananas and pineapple for sale, and war it was between the dining-car staff and conductor, fighting the crowd from the station who wanted to break into the car. The crowd won and cleared it out of pineapples and bananas, so starved of fruit are the Russians.

This party was now into the third round of fritters and when I left looked as if they would never stop.

CHAPTER FOUR

The Way of the East

BANTU Africa, which lies east of the Rift, would be far greater geographically than West Africa were it not for European history. It would have begun almost at the base of the Ethiopian escarpment and stretched all the way south to the Transkei in the Union of South Africa. Moreover, where the Rift peters out it would have included the larger part of Zaire, all the country that lies between it and the centre and the coast, right down to the Namib desert of the south-west. It would also have included most of Angola except the water-shed of the Congo where Negro Africa still dictates the character of the land. The population of this immense tract is largely of Bantu origin. The problem is that the European grip on most of the people has been so firm and long, European influence has so transformed Bantu society and thinking that much of what would still have been Bantu Africa over a hundred years ago, has to be considered as two provisionally separate wholes. I call one the Portuguese world in Africa and the other the South African sphere, since it extends far beyond political boundaries and penetrates deep into the interior as far north as the Copper Belt of Zambia, the Zambezi river and almost to the shores of Lake Malawi. As a result, the authentic Bantu Africa which remains shrinks into the states created out of the old British East Africa: Kenya, Uganda and Tanzania, including of course the off-shore islands of Pemba and Zanzibar, in spite of their Arab beginnings.

Even so the area is vast enough. Kenya itself is bigger than France; Uganda is roughly the size of West Germany and Tanzania, the biggest of the three, is almost one-ninth the size of the United States. As in Negro Africa the generalisation Bantu, a term which identifies races on a linguistic basis, covers a bewildering variety of humanity. It contains some 220 main tribes, not counting colourful little fragments of what once used to be great races, scattered like confetti among them. Except for the Baganda in Uganda, who, until recently, formed a kingdom with a long and meticulous although verbally transmitted sense of the past, history in this part of Africa has no conscious meaning and exists almost entirely as tribal psychology and prejudices of unknown origins. The Europeans who controlled Bantu Africa came there barely a hundred years ago and though they transformed the primitive economy and awakened in the people an acute desire for a way of life of their own, there were no such age-old cultures to build on as for instance among Ghanaians, Yoroba, Camaroonians, Ashanti and the subtle peoples of Dahomey and Benin. The Arabs who preceded the Europeans and for some thousand years dominated the East African coastline should have had a more lasting influence. But the positive effects of their contact were cancelled by the cruellest of all trafficking in slaves which they organised from Zanzibar and conducted so exclusively that traders like Tippu Sahib penetrated not only south to Lake Malawi but also right through the heart of Africa and across to the West Coast of Kinshasa and Angola. The slavers, more than anybody else, were the reason why Bantu man did not evolve so much as the Negro because they left primitive society perpetually on the run and never gave it a chance to put down roots of its own.

The result was that when the Europeans took over in East Africa they found either disintegrating or grossly retarded societies. For all the just criticism that can be levelled against their colonialism, the progress made in the comparatively short period of European rule is a tribute both to it and the natural capacities of the Africans. East Africa today is one of the best administered and most progressive areas of the new Africa. So far it seems to have dealt with the divisive urges of tribalism better than West Africa. Cities like Nairobi, Dar-es-Salaam and Kampala were always more to my taste than any in West Africa, with the exception perhaps of Dakar and Abidjan. The one comparison, somewhat odious to East Africa, is that the gap between the African's town and country is even wider than in the West. By far the majority of the peoples on the land still live much as they did when I first came to know them some forty years ago.

What applies in the world of sociology and economy is clearly reflected in the art of cooking. East African man has as yet very little of his own invention to give to the art. The middle classes, which have played such a role in the evolution of eating habits in West Africa, are small and still developing. In so far as they exist they tend to imitate the pattern of cooking set by their imperial predecessors. Until a decade ago the roles normally performed by the middle classes in a modern society, traders, clerks, civil servants, craftsmen, skilled artisans and engineers, were carried out under European command by the thousands of Indians who accompanied the British into East Africa. Both Europeans and Indians had their own deeply rooted customs and obstinate views of food and, without any attractive alternative from East African society to tempt them, they clung to the habits they brought with them. In so far as they changed they did so merely to the extent in which differences of climate and indigenous raw materials forced them into new ways. Even this compulsion to change was not as great as on the European invaders of West Africa, because the land in the eastern part of the continent provided agricultural opportunities similar to those at home. In addition, East Africa came to have what West Africa never possessed—communities of foreign settlers who naturally tended to reinforce in one another the pattern of cooking they had brought with them from their countries of origin. In fairness to them, however, it must be said that by the time these communities had produced children and grandchildren, the recognition of the nature of the Africa to which they were committed was becoming more and more evident in their attitude to cooking. But the significant fact remains that to this day the transforming influences in this regard came not from Africans but from foreigners.

The first, of course, was Arab and was exercised for a thousand years, perhaps even longer, from the Arab strongholds on the islands of Zanzibar and Pemba. It was most pronounced in the coastal areas which became Arab colonies and once had great Arab harbours and prosperous cities, now reclaimed by the jungle. When I first visited East Africa fifty years ago this influence was still strong. It is less so today, since the revolution and the massacre of all prominent people of Arab affinity in Zanzibar some years ago. Zanzibar today, as far as Europeans like myself are concerned, is a closed, barbarous society which ordinary people cannot enter. I tried to do so some years ago but was not, happily as I now think, allowed to leave the airport. To what extent Arab ways still persist in Zanzibar and Pemba, its sister island, I cannot say. But with the disappearance of its own variation of Arab culture, the Arab contribution to cooking has diminished even in my day. Yet as we shall see, valuable traces of it remain and I believe will always remain. For instance, the Arabs brought the spices of the East with them and established a taste for them in East African cooking to a far greater extent than in West Africa. They also introduced rice, dates, raisins and other Eastern fruits which could be preserved only by sun-drying before the age of the refrigerator.

In Tanzania, the greatest tract of all, the incentive of the cook to change should have been German because the first missionaries to establish themselves there were from Germany, and until 1918 it was a German colony. The capital, Dar-es-Salaam—the haven of peace—when I first sailed into it in 1926 was a neat, ordered little city of white-walled houses with red-tiled roofs, cloistered around a church spire and might have been a village lifted straight from Bavaria and magically transported into a world of sparkling jungle and radiant palm. In the clubs and hotels ashore one still drank German beer and schanpps, and could eat dishes like hasen peffer, produced with the incomparable flair the Germans have for cooking game and venison. But when I was in Tanzania a few years ago, neither in Dar-es-Salaam nor anywhere else in the vast territory could I discern any trace of German influence in the cooking. The trouble evidently was that the German concept of colonialisation was too Prussian and militaristic. It shut out indigenous societies so effectively that there was never any question of cultural, let alone gastronomic dialogue between them. There is proof of their approach still visible today in the administrative centres they established, large, solid, stone forts quite unlike the frail bungalows with open verandahs and sash-windows erected by British administrators. When the Germans left, the impulse to continue their tradition of cooking quickly declined in the small hotels, the clubs and the homes of the settlers they left behind. The hotels in any case were largely run by Greeks who, with their instinctive adaptability and without any great tradition of cooking of their own, quickly fell into the muscular ways of the British who followed them and the Indians whom they employed. Already firmly entrenched in their privileged base in the highlands of Kenya and with a middle class of some hundreds of thousands of Indians, the British and the Indian concepts of food took absolute charge of the modern kitchen. This alliance of Anglo-Saxon and Indian in Africa moreover was already based on an honourable precedent and a happy one. The British, after hundreds of years in the East, had not only made their peace with Indian cooking but developed such a liking for it that Indian curries, kedgerees, poppadums, Bombay duck, chapatties, rice and mango chutney were a national feature in England and not even a second-rate boarding house could afford to omit them from their menus. East African cooking starts therefore with roots in three separate systems: the oldest, Arab, the second, Indian and finally, toughest of all, in every sense, British.

One last generalisation: cooking in East Africa can be properly understood only by taking into consideration the grim reality of African existence when the European era first began. The diet of the African consisted largely of meal made out of indigenous millets, sorghums, bananas, and milk, usually in the form of curds and whey. To this was added maize, which the Europeans introduced to Africa. The great paradox of this diet is the almost total absence of meat. For here in East Africa we are in the greatest game area on earth. Yet even more than in Negro Africa cattle, sheep and goats were a form of capital and currency rather than a source of food except in so far as the cattle provided milk. Cattle were only slaughtered for meat when some overwhelming tribal ethic demanded it, some primitive religious need for living sacrifice to appease the spirits of the land or a ceremonial occasion of the utmost importance. The Nilotics of East Africa, the most natural cattle-men of all, set the standard in this regard for their Bantu countrymen. Their cattle were sacred. Meat, whether beef or game, was taboo. Nilotics like the Masai lived entirely on milk, occasionally bleeding their cattle, as the tartars of Gengis Khan bled their ponies. But even the Bantu tribes, who were both shepherds and cultivators, had an extra dimension in their attitude to cattle.

They believed that the spirits of their ancestors spoke to them through the cattle. To this day one of the tasks of their witch-doctors is to listen to the sounds the cattle make at night when they are gathered within the corral. They do this in case the sound should suddenly transmit, in a code only they understand, a message of fateful import for the future of the village and the tribe from the ancestral dead. I still know African peoples who, when the owner of a herd of cattle dies, will lead his favourite heifer to the graveside so that the beast can receive the final instruction of his master's spirit for safe-keeping.

It is true that along the coast and by the great lakes men fished and trapped. Even to this day, flying along the coast of East Africa, I am struck by the patterns made by the elaborate traps protruding from mangrove swamps out into the coral seas like fine scribbles of Indian ink on blank sheets of shining paper. But between the sea and the lakes like Victoria, there were no great rivers, as in West Africa, to supply him with fish. Up-country, the real source of meat was in the teeming game, but primitive hunting methods rendered it inadequate. In any case the Europeans, with their passion for conservation, very quickly made it almost impossible for him to kill game for meat without committing a crime.

There were other complications as well. Deep in every Bantu African is a belief that a man cannot eat the meat of an animal without in some way incorporating the character of the animal into his own self. He is convinced that you become what you eat. One tribe will readily eat zebra meat and a neighbouring one will not touch it. Antelope, which is a delicacy in one region, will be strictly taboo in another. I have a vivid recollection of a company of Free French spahis I met on their way to French Somaliland in the war. They almost caused a mutiny among the African bearers because their offices persuaded me to try a casserole of crocodile cooked in red Algerian wine. To these bearers the crocodile was sacred, as it is to many tribes in Africa. The incident did not worry me so much as make me suddenly and violently homesick because three thousand miles away to the south, on the edge of the Kalahari desert, I knew of a Bantu tribe who had never seen crocodiles but who nonetheless called themselves: "Bakwena"—Men of the Crocodile. It was a startling illustration of the oneness of Africa, the underground telepathy which continues to exist in spite of the social and political forces that work against it on the surface. To this day there is not a race or tribe in Bantu Africa which is not affected to some degree by similar taboos. In East Africa such prejudices sometimes stretch even to fish which a nation of warriors like the Zulus, for instance, will not eat because they believe it turns the heart of a warrior to water.

By an odd coincidence one of my earliest experiences of East African food concerns the oldest of the three basic traditions I have mentioned—the Arab. I first came to Zanzibar and the coast of East Africa the way history came to it—from the East. My ship, a Japanese tramp, came upon the island at dawn. It was not particularly spectacular as islands go but it was balm and comfort to eyes tired of watching a blank, glittering, inert ocean. Our last glimpse of land had been the jungles of Sumutra rolling in the blue of evening like smoke down from the mountains inland to the Straits of Malabar.

All round us were the dhows that are still built, wooden nails and all, as they were a thousand years ago. The scene looked very much as it might have done when Vasco de Gama first broke so brutally into those waters, four hundred years before. As we rounded the headland, the sun rose, the sky flashed like a mirror and there was a little Arab city going down, tidy and compact, to the rim of the harbour front. We dropped anchor and when the rattle of the chains ceased I suddenly realised two things: that it was my lucky day, December 13th, and that a subtle perfume, strangely familiar and provocative although I could not name it, was coming from the coral shore and the gleaming white warehouses. It took me a good minute to realise it was the scent of cloves. The realisation, slight as it was, evoked an immense vista of history because it was the hunger for spice in Europe that had led to the discovery of the New World, the establishment of my own ancestors at the Cape of Good Hope and the first appearance of the Portuguese in these tranquil coral waters.

Zanzibar and Pemba made their history out of trading in slaves and spice. The slavery had gone but the spice remained. Shortly after breakfast, I walked with the captain of the ship to the market-place; the air was so charged with the scent of cloves, it was stifling. The streets beyond the warehouses were constricted and teemed with a new kind of man: part Arab, part African, yet still so identi-fied with his Asiatic origins that he wore a kaffia on his head and a curved golden dagger, like a crescent moon, at his waist. The three-storeyed houses with their narrow windows and Scheherezade balconies had massive doors of superbly carved wood. Imported from the Arabian mainland they were as ornamental as they were securely defensive.

It was difficult to accept that Africa was so new, especially when I accompanied the captain to a meal with the old Sultan who ruled the island. The captain was more than just the master of a cargo ship. In reality he was a plenipotentiary of his country which in those days had a secret dream of an African empire. He was received as such by the Sultan and I, who went along I think largely as a kind of camouflage, sat down with him to an ambassadorial banquet.

The Palace itself was built in a style I came to call tea-planter's manorial. As we were foreigners, we ate in the European manner, with cutlery, rather than our right hands. European appearances, however, were only knife-deep. First of all the banquet was an all-male affair. The servants who brought in the food were pitch-black and later in the day I was to pick up the insistent whisper that they were still slaves in all but name, and eunuchs to boot. The only hints of feminine presence were odd glimpses I caught of saffron-coloured faces with large black eyes made larger and darker by a liberal use of mascara, peering curiously and furtively at our table, then vanishing as they caught my eye. The food too was far from European and of a kind that I had never encountered before. As might have been expected in the Sultan's palace, it was the best the island could produce.

The main foundation of the meal was rice. It was accompanied by fish, mutton and, above all, a supremely roasted chicken. The fish and the mutton as far as I remember were not exceptional but the chicken course deserves a paragraph to itself. First of all, however, there was the rice. The savour of it is still with me. I was from a country where rice is eaten as a matter of course at all main meals. Moreover, I had just come from the greatest rice countries of the world, Japan, China, the Straits of Malacca, India and Ceylon—yet I had never eaten rice like it. The first experience of anything in life, just by virtue of being first, has a unique impact. I was to eat similar rice in Mombasa, in the ancient Arab port of Lamu and in Dar-es-Salaam but it never compared to that first experience in Zanzibar.

All that escapes me is the Zanzibari name, although I was told it the same evening at another meal in the house of a merchant family from Karachi. They told me it was rice cooked in the ancient Persian manner and that the Sultan, who claimed descent from the highest aristocracy of Persia, always served this rice at state banquets to proclaim the ancient origin of his house.

One of many reasons for trying to get back to Zanzibar was to try to rescue this form of rice from the oblivion into which the brutal revolution in the island threatened to cast all things Arab. I have discovered, however, somewhat to my amazement, that this method of cooking rice had been resurrected and is still alive in

Kenya. The person mainly responsible was a young German chef in Nairobi who had not only been to Zanzibar but cooked in Persia as well. The rice I had first eaten there, he was certain, was a version of what is called celo rice in Persia. He was even more lyrical about it than I was, calling it a dish out of the tale of a thousand and one nights. I told him that the impression made on my palate was so acute and original that I was certain it must have been made from a very special sort of rice. He assured me that even in Persia it was just a variety of Patna rice and that he had cooked it in his grand hotel in Nairobi with equal success from Carolina rice. All he emphasised was that in Zanzibar and along the East African coast the rice, grown in tropical conditions, must inevitably give the best results.

He mentioned five elements that were of fundamental importance to the success of the dish: patience, time—from start to finish in his estimation you could not do the dish in less than twelve hours —rice consisting only of unblemished grain, water with a considerable content of chalk and a wood fire. The royal household of Zanzibar was so full of servants, to say nothing of a harem full of idle women, that time and patience could not have been lacking, and this would explain why the rice served there was so good. I can understand that the modern cook's impatient imagination might boggle at the preparation and the labour involved, just as I am convinced that once a gourmet tried such rice he would insist on having it again and again. For the truth is that in cooking as in all other problems of living, short cuts are retrogressive, leading only to increasingly barbaric solutions. In the kitchen, the longest way round is still the shortest way to the perfect dish.

I learned how this young chef would get his assistants to select each grain of rice specially some twelve hours before cooking the dish. Any grain that was in the least bit damaged or mis-formed was rejected and when the collection was complete the rice was washed thoroughly twice. I reminded him of an Italian kitchen proverb: "Wash your face, wash your hands, wash your feet but never wash rice because rice is not proud." He dismissed this with scorn as another example of how the Mediterraneans undercook everything from beef and lamb to rice and pasta. He went on to explain that the twice-washed rice was placed in a flat dish, just covered with water and layers of white clean linen pressed into the dish to protect it from dust. On top of the linen some rock salt was put, both to keep the linen pressed down firmly on the rice and also to impart its own savour, through the damp cloth, to the grains. So dedicated a cook was he that he preferred one form of rock salt to all others—it was gathered in an Asiatic desert and it gave the dish, he claimed, something no other salt could. Two hours before cooking, the rice was extracted from the dish and washed again, parboiled until it whitened and then drained. The rice was then put, in layers, in a large iron pot—in Persia the pot is of copper—and each layer covered with small lumps of butter or ghee, until the pot was about three-quarters full. It was then covered again with several folds of dry cloth, in order to absorb and seal in the steam. It was most important, he said, that the lid of the pot should be made to fit so that no steam could escape.

The rice was then cooked over a wooden fire, not only from underneath the pot but also by charcoal placed on the lid. The great secret was to ensure that the rice was cooked at a constant temperature. He said that a dedicated cook in Persia would not allow even an earthquake to distract him from attending in person to this phase of the operation. Patiently, squatting by his fire, he would watch the flame, one minute encouraging the heat by fanning the coals with a palm leaf, the next damping it down with a dash of water and constantly renewing the live coals on the lid. All this lasted about an hour and when the lid was finally removed one would see that the rice had risen to the brim, white and light as snow in the middle and at the sides just faintly bronzed, with each grain of rice doubled in size. It was then ready to be served, steaming and fragrant. And that, precisely, is how the Sultan offered it to us in Zanzibar.

The modern cook who has no time to spare for cooking rice in this classic way can come near to the idea by doing it in a casserole in an oven where it can get heat both from below and on top and, of course, where the temperature can be regulated even more accurately.

Finally, a word about the Sultan's chicken. This had been done to crisp perfection. The skin had obviously been pricked all over with a sharp needle and properly basted with butter in a very hot oven, before being removed and finished off in a cast iron pot with a mixture of water and pomegranate juice in just sufficient quantities to prevent it from burning. When the chicken was finally cooked and ready the juice of the pomegranate and water that remained had been thickened with walnuts, minced and fried.

A feature of this banquet too was the fruit which accompanied it: pineapples like Japanese lanterns, ripe papayas like rugby footballs, mangoes, guaves, pomelow, bananas and pomegranates. The pomegranates had clearly travelled a long way but fortunately they keep very well in their tough, waterproof skins. In my own part of Africa, we store them in our attics to provide us with something fresh for the long winters and they have an important role in our eating habits. They may have been a native of the Middle East and Solomon in all his glory used them as a great metaphor in his resounding songs, but they have also migrated to Africa and become an indispensable part of our native scene.

From Zanzibar we went to Mombasa and its harbour of Kilindini. The rock and coral fort built by Vasco da Gama stood there prominently to mark our course and the white and pink plaster of its walls burnt faintly among banana groves and palms on the edge of the sea. Today you have to search for it among the luxury hotels and min-skyscrapers of the growing city. In those days Mombasa looked so unprepossessing that I preferred to live in the tidy Japanese world of our cargo ship and was more than happy to take the first train into the interior. From the start the journey was a revelation of how muscular the British approach to East Africa still was in the twenties. The first class compartments of the train were almost entirely occupied by the Nairobi Rugby Club and their followers, who had been playing a match in Mombasa. I had been a keen and not unsuccessful rugby player myself in South Africa, yet I was amazed that men could play so exciting a game on the equator. The incident was a mirror reflecting in miniature the profound nostalgia of the European in Africa for the country of his origin and his resulting determination to bend Africa to his ways.

The journey was memorable too because it was my first experience of how the British fed in Africa. There were no dining cars and for dinner the train was halted at a siding called Tsavo. This siding had a gruesome fame of its own. A Colonel Patterson, who was the prototype of the main character in Ernest Hemingway's *The Macomber Affair* (filmed as "The Snows of Kilimanjaro"), told the story in his *The Man Eaters of Tsavo*. During the construction of the railway, work was held up for weeks by man-eating lions who preyed on the Indian coolies. The lions became so arrogant that they even entered the railway coaches parked in the siding, battered down the doors and dragged people out of the compartments. An Indian station-master, clocking in for duty one evening, found his platform in the possession of a pride of lions. He locked himself in his office and tapped out an S.O.S. to Nairobi in the immortal words: "Beg to report man-eating lions in possession of station. Kindly await instructions."

The lions happily were not in possession of the station the evening I stopped at Tsavo. But at dinner they were roaring in the night round about us so that at moments talk was impossible. In the cramped station dining-room we sat, grimly silent, behind mosquito nets. The tables were crowned in the centre with bottles of tomato ketchup, crude cruets of salt, pepper and vinegar, and bottles of Worcestershire sauce made, as the tags informed us, from "a recipe by a nobleman of the county". This was the sauce which inspired Voltaire's remark: "In England they have 120 different religions but only one sauce, in France we have only one religion but 120 sauces."

However, on this evening I felt no incentive to laugh at the bottle of sauce on my table, just as I had no desire to make fun of my rugby-playing companions, because the bottle on the stained railway table-cloth seemed to symbolise a fundamental concept that governed the English kitchen. I remember that our meal started with a brown meat consommé, strongly flavoured with Bovril, followed by fried fish and sweet-potato chips, followed by boiled silverside of meat, dumplings, onions and carrots and rounded off with rice pudding and stewed prunes. This appeared to be standard railway fare. On my journey back from Nairobi some time later, the train stopped for dinner at a station called Simba—the Swahili for lion—where setting, food, everything was an exact replica of Tsavo even to the roaring of the lions outside.

There was obviously no concession to Africa in this way of eating but what was far more significant was the fact that, on both occasions, my fellow passengers fell on this tough, indifferently-cooked fare as if they were being presented with the greatest delicacies.

However, there were more important things even than food for me to think about because at dawn I found myself at the window of my compartment looking out on one of the most beautiful parts of Africa. Even now, having seen it a score or more of times and after constantly journeying backwards and forwards throughout the continent objectively, I have to admit it is the most beautiful of all despite the claims of my own native South Africa and all the inborn prejudices that make it first in my emotions and senses.

The country was high, open to the sky and moulded to distance and uncluttered space. The jungle of the coast had vanished, the tangled bush around Tsavo had gone and as far as one could see the world had been taken over by yellow grass and a flawless horizon pinned down with hills of blue almost as if nature were afraid that so high and ethereal a plain would become airborne and be translated into sky. Away to the south there was the strangely Japanese outline of Kilimanjaro, elegaic under snow and blue as Fujiama in a wood-cut by Hokusai. Snow may be a commonplace of Europe and America and inspire no poetic emotion, but its appearance here on the equator, especially when seen from the window of a train in which we could hardly breathe for the fine red dust thrown up by the wheels, was a miracle. But that was not all, for soon, far away to the north-west, in the clear sparkling morning air, appeared the mitred summit of the other giant hill, Kenya, not with a crown but a bright feather of snow in its peaked cap. It was almost as if nature, before letting loose its chaotic, abundant self on the world, had consulted a mountain planning committee and instead of presenting the mountains in one overwhelming jumble as in Alps, Rockies and Himalayas, had selected two of the best and made all this great yellow plain a royal academy where two could represent the rest.

Karen Blixen and I often talked about this and how superbly and almost consciously nature had played the artist for once in the arrangement of mountain and plain. She had a particularly evocative image for describing the land that lay between Kilimanjaro and Kenya. She said that what she loved best about it was that, after Europe, the landscape was lean and had no fat upon it. Lean as it was to the eye, it was teeming with game in a way I have never since seen Africa, even in the South.

I know there may be other parts of Africa just as crowded but the crowds are lost and hidden in bush and jungle. Here, like the mountains, they were out in the open. The land seemed to be bursting at its blue seams with animal life—elephant in their compact family huddles, inquisitive giraffe at times almost looking in through the railway windows, vast herds of harlequin zebra, restless gnu, purple eland with white dew-laundered socks, antelope and gazelle, their skins a flicker of flame in the yellow grass. Yet this was only a fragment of the natural animal and its setting. I was to complete the picture later by journeys beyond Mount Kenya in the North-West Frontier District, camping at places called after forgotten pioneers like Archer's Post and Kittermaster's Camp, and so north to Lake Rudolph and east to the black lava deserts and waste-lands of the Somali.

The names of these great lakes alone evoked the whole period which produced the men who brought them into the awareness of the Western world. Rudolph, its neighbour Stephanie, Victoria, Edward and Albert, all read like names lifted at random from the *carnet du bal* of a debutante summoned to a ball by the great white queen in whose name all this vast land was once administered. These lakes were as full of life, of crocodiles, hippopotami and fish as the plains were of game. Each had its own particular personality and speciality. Some were deep, volcanic and so charged with minerals like magadi and natron that they gloried in birds rather than fish; flights of storks, pelicans and white ibis revolving like clouds above them, almost hiding with their wings the lurid dyes of green, saffron, indigo and scarlet colouring their heavy water. Then there were smaller lakes, like Lake Naivasha, so crowded with flamingo that at dawn their waters looked like blazing grass-land. At nightfall in the migrating season these same lakes were packed as tight as any city car park with geese, duck and other wild fowl. Indeed, shooting duck at Christmas on waters like Naivasha became Kenya's equivalent of the glorious twelfth.

North of Kenya, at places like Marsabit where Martin Johnson and his intrepid wife showed cinema-goers all over the world how photogenic the game of Africa is, the scrub and the bush teemed with game like the plains. One would camp in what looked like an empty place but would soon discover that, as always in Africa, one is never alone. No matter how secluded or remote the camp or track there was always some living eye trained on one. One always had what is, for me, one of the exciting things about Africa: the warm feeling that one was travelling through time in a convoy of natural life.

In such a land, with such material available, one would have thought that the Europeans and Indians in Africa, with all they already knew of cooking, would have become the great innovators in the art of preparing game. But it is fantastic what unimaginative use they made of so unique an opportunity. They cooked game in the most obvious ways, treating it very much as they treated beef, mutton and fowl at home and, no wonder, found a great deal of natural material unsuitable. Even to this day their methods of cooking game in East Africa are at best imitations of German and French recipes. There was one exception to the rule. There was among the British a strong nucleus of Boers who had migrated from South Africa after the Anglo-Boer war. They brought with them the South African art of cooking and marinating game. But as their approach is no different from that of their countrymen in the South I will deal with it in that context. All that needs to be stressed here is that their methods were successful because, although there are distinctive East African varieties of game, they were in the main the same as in the South, and not only the game but the domestic animals as well.

Just as many wild animals of Africa like the eland and the greater kudu carry humps on their back where they store reserves of valuable carbohydrates against lean and hungry days, the domestic animals too were humped. The bigger, plumper and looser the hump in cattle, the healthier the condition of the animal was known to be. In fact one could gauge the health of the animal as accurately from the condition of his hump as a doctor can measure the degree of fever in a human patient with a thermometer.

The sheep of the nomads of the North-West Frontier District did not have humps but fat tails which performed the same function. In a season of plenty their tails grew great so that they did not walk so much as waddle. They were the exact replicas of the Hottentot sheep my ancestors encountered in South Africa when they settled there some three hundred years ago and which prompted the national witticism that it was a land where not only the dog but the whole sheep was wagged by the tail. More endearing still, the original man of Africa, the bushman, was similarly equipped by nature. He had a special sort of behind that in a good season grew plump with reserves of fat. My grandfather, who knew the bushmen well, would joke to me as a boy and say he had seen bushmen behinds so large and protuberant that he could stand a bottle of Cape brandy and two glasses upon them.

It is possible that the new invaders of East Africa would have taken the whole of natural Africa more into their imagination and evolved something startlingly original out of it but for four factors.

One, there was the profound nostalgia of which I have spoken, natural enough in the first generations of all exiles and of which rugby players and Worcester sauce were so convincingly an illustration. Two, there was the total failure, through no fault of its own, of aboriginal East African society to hold out a ready-made alternative. Three, in the highlands of East Africa the Europeans found privileged conditions of climate and earth which seduced them into the belief that they could resurrect an ideal of life which had become impossible in the Europe they had left behind. Four, they were never isolated as the Portuguese and the Dutch had been, because regular communication by fast steamships and railway already existed and the aeroplane was so close to binding them even more tightly to the country of their origin that, when I first visited that part of the world, Kikuyu mothers in search of new names for their children were starting to call them "aeroplane".

The British set about re-creating their dream of a new life with astonishing energy and persistence. In the process they suffered enormous losses of money and endured hardships that have never been appreciated among a critical public and a world increasingly sceptical of colonisation. They suffered because the nature of Africa fought back against innovation as it has always done. They started by importing the cereals, vegetables and fruit they needed from Europe and India. They brought domestic animals from Great Britain at vast expense, cows, bulls, sheep, dogs, horses and aimed at being the first gentlemen farmers of Africa. They brought tea from India and Ceylon and began to grow coffee while the South Africans, on their plateau in the heart of the highlands, planted the wheat and the maize they brought with them from the south. The resistance of Africa was so fierce and great that it was only by constantly importing fresh blood both of men and animals from Britain and Europe that they could pursue their idea. Many private fortunes were lost in the process. The idea which made them the subject of an endless series of music-hall jokes in Britain, that these pioneers were merely a pleasure-loving community, I knew from my own experience, applied only to exceptions that proved a *far* different rule. It is true that, in between the battles to establish a world of their own, they kept up their courage by playing games like polo, hunting in scarlet and establishing race-courses. Even more astonishing, they brought their love of fishing with them and rounded off their dream of a squire's life by stocking their rivers with trout. As a result, to this day there are few highland streams in Kenya, Uganda, right down to the southern highlands of Tanzania and the Shire hills of Malawi, which are not stocked with trout.

East Africa, when I knew it, was not a literary world and books were scarce but I do not think I have ever seen so many copies of *The Compleat Angler* anywhere else. Trout appears as a matter of course on tables in the most unlikely circumstances and to this day is eaten in many parts of East Africa as if it were a native of the land. I remember once walking into the White Rhinoceros hotel on the slopes of Mount Kenya just before dinner. The bar was crowded with men telling tall stories, as if they had just come in from a favourite beat on a river in Scotland. It made no difference that Mao Mao was about to burst on the land and that the air was charged with impending disaster, and the future volcanic with momentous change. The minds of these men were entirely concerned with the problems of fishing and the importance of deciding whether they had been told the truth or merely had their legs pulled by an enthusiast who entered at the same time as I did and claimed that with his last cast, in the twilight, his fly had never found the water but had hooked a bat in passing and he had been almost overcome with superstitious awe when he found his reel unwinding rapidly and the line vanishing into space.

But despite all, despite increasing world discouragement, the British came through to a kind of success that was meaningful not only to Kenya but to East Africa as a whole. The whole subject is still too charged with emotion for their achievement to be assessed objectively. One will have to wait for a century or more before that can be done. But of one thing I am certain: when the final assessment is made it will be found that the creative consequences of the European achievement in agriculture and honest administration were more significant for Africa than many other defects of their colonisation.

The quality of the East African experiment was considerably heightened by the fact that the calibre of the British who increasingly participated in it was, humanly speaking, better I believe than in any other colonial effort. I know of no other colony where the so-called gentry and aristocracy of Great Britain played so great a role and in fact set the tone for the rest of the country. Practically all the newcomers were highly individualistic if not eccentric. Some had such streaks of wildness and reckless abandon that they readily reinforced their Vaudeville image at home. Yet there was something oddly Elizabethan about the majority and the great pioneering land-owners like Lord Delamere might have been buccaneers and free-booters of Sir Walter Raleigh's day and indeed with hindsight look so to many. But in the context of their own day, they had no sense of wrong-doing and saw themselves as the instruments of a superior culture, conferring civilisation on a hideously deprived and barbarous land. Lord Delamere for instance, when I first met him, lived in the simplest way and his thatched house was always open to the Africans who called on him regularly night and day. I have seen Masai chiefs arrive confidently, stick their long throwing-spears firmly into the earth by the front door, walk without waiting for an invitation into the front room and sit down like members of a family to talk for hours about some matter that exercised their minds. Discrimination existed of course but in Kenya there was never, in my experience, total exclusion of the African to the extent the Germanic pattern imposed on Tanzania. Again with hindsight one can criticise Kenya for having been too paternalistic but one cannot question that somewhere, subtly at work, there was a great love by the British for the land and its people. When the moment of Independence came for Kenya, the complex system of agriculture established in the highlands was secure and most impressive. Kenya coffee, after the most discouraging beginnings, had become so established that its blends were familiar everywhere in the English-speaking world and coffee houses calling themselves "Kenya" sprang up all over Great Britain.

The annual Royal Agricultural Show—the state fair of East Africa—had nothing to compare with it anywhere on the continent except perhaps the annual show in Johannesburg; one could easily have imagined oneself back in Britain as prize-winning Jerseys, Guernseys, Red Poles, Short Horns, Ayrshires, Aberdeen Anguses and white-faced Herefords paraded by. In fact it all looked so fundamentally European to me that once, sitting at the show with the Governor General of the day, I could not help replying to his exclamation: "It's magnificent, isn't it?" with "Yes sir, but it isn't African animal husbandry, it is *sheer* nostalgia."

Yet the British had begun to learn to take the African more seriously and to shed other prejudices against native livestock, like humped-back cattle and fat-tailed sheep. I noticed at one of the last agricultural shows I attended in Nairobi the greatest cheer of all was reserved for the indigenous animals in the parade.

All the history of East Africa is summed up for me in the story of one man who helped to bring this transformation about. Brian Curry was one of my oldest friends. I tell his story in detail because it reflects that of many. He went to East Africa, as many did, immediately after the First World War. He had served in the trenches, had been badly wounded and gone back to a rich family home deeply disillusioned with Europe and profoundly depressed by so much killing. He had gone out to Kenya and started farming not on the privileged highlands but beyond Mount Kenya where the great Northern Frontier District begins. There he tried to do what all the other British in Kenya were doing, to breed only what was best in English sheep and cattle. His efforts were disastrous. Year after year he imported the finest breeds from England and had to watch them go into decline and ultimately waste away in the African environment. He lost a fortune in the process. One day, out on his ranch, in a state of despair and near bankruptcy, looking at his diminishing cattle, he saw that while they were lying in the shade of the thorn trees, panting for breath, the indigenous humped-backed cattle of his Boran herdsmen were grazing, sleek, fat and happy under the noon-day sun. He realised in a flash that he had been guilty of exercising the same prejudices against the indigenous domestic animals as against the primitive ways of Africa. There and then he got rid of all his European cattle and with such money as he had left, bought Boran cattle and set about selecting and breeding them in the same scientific way that had established the great breeds of Europe. The results were immediate and exciting. Some of his neighbours combined with him in the experiment and before long they had established in East Africa what it had previously lacked, a sort of tropical Aberdeen Angus. The experiment prospered to the point where, at the time of Independence, he was breeding Boran cattle with white coats and black skin-pigmentation which is the ideal protection against the equatorial sun. Moreover the experiment was such a success that governments like that of Brazil, faced with the problem of breeding beef and cattle in tropical conditions, are more and more buying their bulls from breeders like him.

I tell this story too because it explains why Kenya became the first African country north of the Limpopo to produce barons of beef, under-cuts and fillets that can compare with the best Europe, not excluding the United States of America, has to offer. The beef may be slightly darker and the marbling different but the taste and tender texture are as good if not better. As well as cattle and sheep, the highlands produce pigs with such success that the bacon and ham of the country are as good as in Britain and produced in such quantities that wherever one goes in East Africa, in Tanzania or Uganda, the ham and bacon one eats is of Kenyan origin. Nor should one forget the formidable development of dairying which enables East Africa to produce its equivalents of the best known European cheeses from Cheddar to Camembert and gorgonzola. But then, as an African, I am prejudiced in this regard. Yet prejudice is over-ruled by objectivity because, when Brian Curry died, the present Kenya Government thought that his work was of such value that they brought his great ranch for their National Development Organisation.

What Kenya achieved in cattle breeding it also did in agriculture. In time, all European vegetables became readily available so that the cook could serve, as a matter of course, delicacies like straw-berries and asparagus that had been grown in the land and not flown in, as in the Congo. At diplomatic dinners in Dar-es-Salaam and Kampala, cherished luxuries like strawberries and asparagus are flown in from Nairobi, not from Europe. As with animals and vegetables, so it was with flowers. In the gardens the English made wherever they went in the world the flowers were a kind of badge of their determination to remain a part of England. They grew roses, hollyhocks, sweet Williams, larkspur, carnations and gladioli as lovely as any in Britain. With all this, it is not surprising that the European went his own original way and that the example of living and eating he left behind him and which dominates the taste of the new Africa, should have been of the cooking he brought with him into his exile.

What made the impact of his example even more profound was the fact that he trained the Bantu of East Africa to be his cooks, butlers and domestic servants. Indeed there is no other part of Africa where the home was so entirely dominated by the male. Considering the deep prejudices Africans have against domestic labour, even to the extent of regarding the tilling of the land as women's work, this in itself is a great tribute to the quality of the personal relationship established between European and African man. By the time of Independence, the seventy-odd thousand Europeans had homes that were entirely run by African males.

In fact the intrusion of any sort of feminine presence in that world was so keenly resisted that many a European bachelor, when he married, found his African servants walking out *en masse*. This aspect of life is more significant than it sounds because, though the European and his Indian ally are fast being eliminated from the economic life of the land and the numbers of European farmers have sharply declined, there are these enormous reserves of African cooks they trained at work everywhere in the new Africa. Their influence must inevitably be profound. Also since they were trained by men who originally came from homes where standards of service were exceedingly high, the Bantu of East Africa have acquired standards higher than anywhere else in the continent. One can arrive at an East African airport or walk into an East African hotel, where today these things are organised almost entirely by Africans and be impressed, as nowhere else, by the order, cleanliness and courtesy.

I have mentioned the number of cookery books produced by missionaries and others in the old British West Africa. In the whole of East Africa there has only been one to help the indigenous cook: *The Kenya Settlers Cookery Book and Household Guide*. It was first published in 1928, two years after my own encounter with East African food on the railway siding at Tsavo. It has gone through twelve editions since and in the process becomes a formidable household guide not just in Kenya but all over East Africa and as far south as Malawi and Zambia. It still features in most bookshops in East Africa but it looks increasingly lonely on the shelves where its dark blue cover and gold lettering are completely out-shone by spectacular books on all forms of cooking except that of Africa. In the biggest bookshop in Nairobi some years ago I counted 100 glossies on all the world systems of cooking from Chinese to Italian but this book remained, as it was for the pioneers, the one and only one to speak up for East Africa. It makes curious and historic reading because there is hardly any African inspiration in it. It just seems to say in cold, disdainful words what I have so often been told by European housewives when I asked them what Africans ate—"Oh, they just eat posho"—that is a thick doughy porridge made out of maize flour. As for the Masai or the Kamarojo, the answer would invariably be a horrified: "Do you know, they don't cook at all. They bleed their cattle at the neck and mix up the blood with curds and whey and gulp it down. It makes you thoroughly sick to watch them."

The men would have more robust reactions. These were mostly the District Commissioners who were one of Britain's most worthwhile inventions in Africa. They would so identify themselves with the tribes to whom they were attached as to become virtually the most formidable tribalists of all. For instance I knew district officers attached to the Masai who would fight their opposite numbers attached to the Kavirondo as if they were not colleagues in the colonial service but enemies of diabolic dye. They would tell you with delight how they had enjoyed a dish of locusts fried in the fat extracted from the tail of a black-nosed sheep in the Northern Frontier District or caterpillars and grubs extracted from dead trees in the bush and suitably rendered in ground nut oil. In Uganda, above all, they would speak of the taste of some tribes for termites. This taste incidentally existed all over Africa and is not to be despised if one is hungry in bush or jungle. I knew it well from my childhood. In the south we called it "bushman's rice"— because the termites (in fact the South Africans call them rice-ants) were curiously white and rice-like in appearance. They had a sharp tartaric flavour and, when fried, even in tinned butter, went down well with roast venison. In fact, in some of the capitals of Europe today, specially prepared termites are on sale in tins, and the Japanese in particular have developed a liking for them. Once in Japan I ate African termites enclosed, like nuts, in chocolate.

The best informed District Commissioners might even have mentioned how the tiny Ndorobo, who were perhaps the aborigines of East Africa, have their own way of curing venison and eating it dipped in wild honey. This wild honey is more exciting even than the semi-domesticated Ethiopian variety. The bees that produce it are the fiercest and most unpredictable in the world. They will attack a traveller without provocation, often stinging him to death. When I was doing exploration work for the British Government not long after the war, the bees' favourite target seemed to be visiting anthropologists—by preference lady anthropologists—but happily without fatal results. Something of the wildness, one is almost inclined to say passion, of these tiny bees seems to enter into the taste of the honey, making it the most unusual I know. The instinct which led the Ndorobo to eat their meat in this way has proved so popular that this recipe ultimately found its way into the cooking of game in East Africa after the war. I have had roast fillets of gazelle served not with red-currant jelly but chunks of wild honey, with rice and cabbage.

The Kenya Settlers Cookery Book and Household Guide contains no recipes for preparing indigenous foods. Yet not only are there two different recipes for making something so unrelated to Africa as haggis but, in case these should fail, also one for a "mock haggis". The compilers too have included all the main traditional British dishes as well as many Indian and some South African ones as well. Only one game soup is mentioned. Its only concession to Africa apart from the raw material is that some cloves are added to the brew. The recipe, however, ends with the ominous injunction that the soup should be thickened with flour and that the flavour will be improved by the addition of port wine or Bovril. This of course is barbaric prejudice because African game soup, simmered slowly with onions, peppers, cloves and seasoning can be delicious. If wine has to be used, a dry Madeira or a dry South African sherry, both of which are much closer to the soil and nature of East Africa, will produce better results than port.

More significant still, although this book has recherché recipes for shellfish, like lobster Newburg or lobster Thermidor, it has no specific African recipes for the superb shellfish of the coast, or the game and wild fowl. Even the marinating processes, so common among the grain-growing settlers from southern Africa, do not get a mention. The reader of the handbook, who is so minutely inducted into the mysteries of mayonnaise and *sauce hollandaise*, is simply commanded to roast, grill or stew his game as if it were exactly like the domestic equivalents in Europe.

As is to be expected from the greater breed within the law which carried Worcester sauce and tomato ketchup wherever it went, the imagination of the compilers of this book was stimulated most by the opportunities East Africa provides for evolving new species of ketchups, chutneys and pickles. This is one feature of early pre-war East African cooking I recollect with real pleasure: the great varieties of really good home-made chutneys and ketchups that were served with increasingly good hams and other cold meats. First and perhaps most obvious of all came the banana chutneys. There was also a particularly good mixed chutney made out of guavas, apples, bananas, stoned raisins and apricots, and there were as many home-made mango chutneys and green mango ketchups as there were varieties of mango. I remember also the pickled aubergine or, to give it the Indian name by which it is known, the brinjaul.

The brinjaul has become so much a part of the East African diet that it deserves a mention on its own. It is so cheap and easy to grow that its place in the future of cooking is well assured. It is commonly eaten curried, with rice, and no doubt it still appears in many East African homes as an accompaniment to bacon and eggs, fried simply in bacon fat or done in a light batter. There are countless other variations as well. Whatever has happened to the Indians in East Africa and the customs they brought to the country, brinjauls, I am certain, like other forms of Indian curries and spices will remain part of the cooking of the land.

Other old favourites of Indian inspiration, I see from a recent edition of the handbook, still hold their own as savouries. For instance there is an old friend that appeared as regularly at the end of meals in country hotels as Welsh rarebit in English boarding houses: rajah's toast. It is a grand name but really an impostor, being merely ham paste flavoured with curry powder, sprinkled with a favourite chutney, chopped, spread on hot buttered toast, and warmed under the grill. I could multiply the examples, but these I hope are enough to show on what rough foundations the East African cook had to build a kitchen of his own. Yet he has done it so successfully that, looking back on the way I fed there some forty-three years ago, it seems almost part not so much of real experience as of a kind of dream, if not nightmare, of the kitchen.

On the coast now the cook makes the most of the unique harvest of crustaceans and fish the coral seas provide. The giant crabs, the small dark oysters, compensating like all things small for their lack of size with an assertive taste and character of their own, imperial prawns, shrimps, lobster, crayfish, magnificent sea-bream and scores of other varieties now get the civilised treatment they have so long deserved. Kilindini oysters baked in their own juice on a fire of driftwood are just about as good a beachcomber dish as one can find anywhere in the world, so much so that East African hotels and restaurants readily serve them as appetisers to a main meal. Shrimps and prawns shelled and cooked, mixed with a judicious amount of finely diced pineapple and lemon mayonnaise and served in the shell of the pineapple look as good on an East African table as they taste.

One of the most spectacular revelations of how things have changed for the better in the cooking of East Africa came to me some years ago when I stayed in the beach home of a friend of mine in Lamu. Lamu is an ancient and beautiful little Arab harbour on the coast north of Mombasa. It seems to entice and gather around it all that is best in the different strands of culture that have been woven into the history of Bantu Africa. My friend is a bachelor and still lives far away on the edge of the great Rift Valley in a home built for him fifty years ago by a Finnish ship's carpenter. But every year he comes to Lamu and brings his own cook with him. The cook is a Knipsigis, a member of one of the minor tribes of East Africa. He was born in a thatched mud hut, has had no education in our sense of the word and yet is a natural cook of distinction. He had evolved his own way of doing the king prawns of the east coast. He would shell them and spike them on a thin bamboo skewer sandwiched between squares of streaky Kenya bacon. He would grill them over highly aromatic charcoal while he prepared some fried rice. He did this by frying the rice in ground nut oil until it was brown and then adding water drop by drop to the rice in the pan until it was just cooked, each grain separate and yet done to a turn. The prawns and rice were served together just as they were or with a mild curry sauce or a peanut sauce made highly piquant by the addition of chopped red peppers. I felt certain that somewhere far back the Arabs of Lamu had something to do with this combination of shellfish and rice because they appear combined in many variations from Lamu all down the east coast to the old Lourenço Marques in Mozambique and South Africa. If one has to have a vegetable with crustaceans, rice is the winner. Sometimes the Knipsigis, instead of frying his rice, served it flavoured with saffron or turmeric. This, I am certain, was originally an Indian inspiration, but all these methods are extremely good.

I am glad to say that at last the cooking of venison is taken more seriously. The gazelle, the impala, the eland, the kudu and the buffalo have always figured, in a somewhat crude and obvious way, on the standard Kenyan menu. But there were many other worthy varieties left in the cold—the zebra—I have eaten first rate zebra casseroles in the south—the warthog, unprepossessing as he appears, the hippopotamus and even the elephant as some of the indigenous peoples, in their simple way, found to be edible. But the few Europeans who ventured into this wider realm seemed to me to be motivated more by curiosity than a desire for the fulfilment of real taste. They created what I call "curiosity cooking", so much so that I remember an old Central African joke which was taken quite seriously by newcomers in the towns. It was said that District Commissioners, out in the bush, always ate a dish of elephant's head and trotters on Sundays. There are many who claim that elephant meat is as good as any other if properly treated. I have often seen my own bearers go wild with excitement when I have had to shoot a rogue elephant. They would eat the elephant as if it were caviare—largely perhaps because their traditional diet is so deprived of meat—feasting over their fires the whole night long like Roman emperors so that in the morning they were overfull and dazed with food. I had the greatest difficulty in persuading them to move on. I have often tried elephant myself and I find it edible but no more. It is, to me, the equivalent in the bush of whale meat at sea but both whale and elephant are I believe, of too giant a texture ever to be truly palatable no matter what method is employed. A stronger case might be made out for selected portions of the elephant. A great favourite of the "curiosity cook" has always been the tip of the tongue and the pads and lower joint of the foot. I have had cold elephant trunk in aspic but even so I do not believe that the elephant can ever play a serious role in the future cooking of Africa, let alone the rest of the world.

The hippopotamus has, as the indigenous people who trap him know, perhaps the finest natural lard of any animal in the world. As a child I knew great hunters who assured me that hippopotamus lard was so sweet and tasty that one could eat it raw and claimed they preferred it that way. There is the giraffe too. I do not know what giraffe meat tastes like but its marrow is perhaps the oldest and most sought-after delicacy of primitive man in Africa. The warthog I am certain, if properly treated, could become for Africa what the wild boar was for Europe and indeed still is in Germany, Poland and the forest of Dom in the south of France. But obviously the greatest contribution to the East African table must come, as it is increasingly coming, from the antelope. One would have thought that the luxury safaris which are better ordered and organised on a far greater scale in East Africa than in any other part of the world, would have been pioneers in the cooking of venison. They started, after all, by taking the privileged people of all nations into the wilds of East Africa where they had the responsibility of feeding them as well as they could. The great Colonel Roosevelt, Maharajas of India, the aristocracy of Great Britain and disappointed Victorian lovers, all were in at the beginning of the great safari tradition, and most of them must have had reasonably cultivated tastes. But strangely enough safari cooking, even at its best, has never been more than an imitation of international hotel fare cooked in a wild African setting. The white hunters who were in charge of these safaris seemed to be more interested in giving their illustrious clients the sort of food they were used to, rather than the food of Africa. I have been on safaris where one was expected, after cocktails, to eat six courses, downed with champagne. The ingenuity that made all this possible was impressive but hardly justified by the indifferent result. I am afraid that this still applies to safari cooking to this day. It is in the homes of the Europeans born in Kenya and in the hotels and restaurants that the real transformation has taken place.

I have had impala as well as Thompson gazelle that were truly delicious. The steaks were cut like tournedos from the back of the gazelle and left to stand for twelve hours in a marinade of dry red South African wine and wild gooseberries. After that, the steaks were well peppered and salted, dusted with flour and browned in butter, and when brown joined with some "waragi", as it is called in Kenya or "waraki" in Uganda. (I imagine the name of this fiery spirit is a corruption of the Araba arak and the great explorer Barber, I recollect, mentioned somewhere how this spirit, brewed from bananas, restored him to health.) Some more butter and berries, either strawberry or blackcurrant, were added and simmered with the steaks until done. I ate my steak with some browned potato croquettes that had some grated fresh coconut and breadcrumbs mixed into them.

I have also had kudu steaks marinaded in a similar manner but served in a sauce made of the natural juices extracted from the steaks in cooking, plus some butter, waragi, wild honey and cream. The sauce was joined to the steaks at the last minute and simmered until it was reduced to a creamy texture. Wild gooseberries or strawberries were then added and the dish served with Kenya rice or minced pistachios. A word of explanation why strawberries in Kenya go so well with game. They have a more precise flavour than any I have ever encountered in Europe and so perform the same function for any heavily roasted meat or venison that redcurrants do in Europe or the quince does in southern Africa.

Finally, having already stressed that East Africa has developed its own indigenous beef equal in quality to anything the Western world can produce, I should add that it is the only part of Africa north of the Limpopo where veal delicate enough for classical treatment is produced. It is not surprising therefore that one encounters veal in restaurants and hotels in all forms from saltimbocca and paillettes, to the immortal schnitzels of Vienna but also in a distinctly East Africa manner as well.

Like strawberries, the mangoes of East Africa deserve a special mention. No doubt they are of Indian origin and one of the greatest contributions of the Indian communities to the land. The mango found itself so at home in East Africa and was so encouraged by the Indians and welcomed by settlers and indigenous peoples that it has spread far and wide and almost as many varieties of it are grown as in the country of its origin. Again it has this special sharp, purposeful, almost savage taste of Africa. In fact there is a large, particularly fleshy, kidney-shaped mango grown in East Africa which to my mind makes a far better beginning to breakfast, lunch or dinner than either melon or grapefruit. Taken cold from the refrigerator and carefully sliced close to the flat stone, it awakes the appetite at breakfast on a hot East African morning just as much as it stimulates the tired palate before dinner at the end of a long day, far more keenly than any fruit I know. Besides, the mango tree beautifies and lends its own dark green lustre to the lean African scene. Indeed, the tree looks as beautiful as its fruit tastes on the table. In the fullness of its season, seen in the heat of the equatorial day, it explains convincingly why, even in Africa, the Lord Buddha chose it to preach his first great green thought, in its green shade, to the burning spirit of his day.

Yet with it all one must still remember how deep a paradox of past and present East Africa remains. Side by side with the feverish urge to become integrated into the contemporary world, there is still the great context of the old primitive Africa that has lain there for so many thousands of years unknown and unknowing in the sun. Much of what remains is what a great old hunter once called "God's country" to me. I would only add one qualification to his remark: it is the country of an Old Testament God. This was very much in the forefront of my mind some years ago when I had to travel north to that strange pagan lake so aptly called Rudolph when one considers it is set in a sort of moonscape which might have been the background for Holman Hunt's painting of the sacrificial goat mentioned in the book of Genesis. There I encountered some East African nomads already on the move at dawn. They came out of the east—the dawn a scarlet shawl wrapped about them—like an illustration of a book of the Pentateuch itself. The tall men, fine-boned and with eyes large, vivid and alive like those of George Borrows's gypsies, walked in a long line in front of a technicolour cavalcade. The men carried quarter-staffs and long throwing spears across their shoulders. Behind them came fat-tailed sheep, with their black noses, like the sheep which figured in the exiled Jacob's wily transaction with his uncle Laban. Behind the sheep came goats and humped-backed cattle with little boys, crackling with energy like a bush fire, urging them along. Behind the boys came camels which seemed twice the height of the Kordufan breed that had taken me into Ethiopia in the war. The girls and the women sat like uncrowned queens on the camels, with the smallest of their children held in front of them. They wore materials of bright vegetable dyes, of the kind in which the young Matisse loved to paint his Moroccan models. They might indeed have been specially posed for an impressionist painting. I spent a day with them and, at night-fall, we came to a water-hole. This was an uncertain and dangerous moment since all their enemies would know how much their attention would have to be given to making certain their cavalcade got the water it badly needed before the quick darkness fell. I shared their suspicion and fear when they saw the water already in possession of other men, as well as the relief when they found that they were kinsmen. Their life was obviously still both harsh and dangerous and yet not without delicacy and culture and a noble sense of hospitality. I ate with them a soup of beans and lentils that may have been the very mess for which Esau, the hunter, sold his heritage to Jacob, the peasant. I drank camel's milk with them and ate the hump of a camel superbly roasted on a wooden fire. The moment might have been set two thousand years before Christ.

A few days later I was back in Nairobi. I was back moreover in an hotel in which I had stayed more than forty years ago. I remember how once, in those remote days, eating an English dinner unworthy of a second-rate boarding house, I was startled by a sudden clatter of horses' hooves and the sight of a woman on horseback bursting into the room. She had on a large hat known in those days as a double terai and was dressed in a khaki riding habit. She had a leather belt round her waist and a pistol in a holster at her hip. She took off her hat and threw it at the startled blonde Norwegian house-keeper in charge of the dining-room, gave her horse to a frightened waiter to hold and called for champagne all round. The champagne was tepid but it was real and helped to heighten my own perception so that to this day I remember the incident almost as an allegory of the strange beginnings of so-called civilisation in this remote and beautiful land.

But on my return a few years ago, I had to shove my way energetically to get at the reception desk, so crowded was the lounge with Greek, Mexican, Spanish and Italian tourists who were due to start out in the morning on mini-buses painted in the zig-zag patterns and colours of the zebra, to stare goggle-eyed at the wild animals of the land. The two-storeyed building I first knew had grown into a mini skyscraper. The dining-room was transformed out of all recognition and in the week I stayed there I could get none of the African foods I have mentioned and which I had eaten in the same hotel at other times, because the hotel was having a French week. Chefs, maîtres d'hôtel, waiters and pretty young Parisian girls to act as guides and hostesses, had been specially flown in from Paris for the occasion. I might have been dining at the Ritz in the Place Vendôme instead of the heart of East Africa. These two extremes express for me not only the paradox but also the changes and the opportunities which confront African man on his road to find a system of living and eating of his own. The danger, I still believe, will ultimately succumb to the opportunity.

CHAPTER FIVE

The Portuguese World in Africa

I ALWAYS used to call it to myself the Portuguese world in Africa. Sheer size and history seemed to make this the only appropriate term and although today that world appears to have vanished forever, I propose to go on using it for the purposes of this book. All men are inclined to see history only in part and in terms of their own brief and brittle measure of life. Only the truly inspired among them know how its processes are unbroken; how it maintains a continuity that stretches inviolate from the first living cell of creation to link our own butterfly ration of reality with all the infinite immensity of what is still to come. For that reason alone I believe that however melodramatic, far-reaching and permanent may appear to be the violent forces of change that have fractured this world in recent years and abolished the political and physical presence of the Portuguese in Africa, the quintessentials of this long, long history will outlive, in the heart of Africa, the changes which swagger so confidently and brutally on the ancient scene.

I say this all the more confidently because these changes were a result not of a deep, passionate and desperate need of the indigenous peoples of Africa but as a consequence of alien pressures both on metropolitan Portugal itself and as a by-product of the confused, muddled and unworthy scramble out of Africa by the British, French and Belgians. It is true that there were, particularly in Mozambique and Portuguese Guinea, so-called indigenous liberation movements at war with the Portuguese, but their leaders were unrepresentative, Europeanised African intellectuals. They would not have succeeded at all had they not been suitably indoctrinated, urged on and actively supported by powerful countries in the outside world, totally unconcerned with the ultimate welfare of Africa and, above all, arrogantly oblivious of the innate dignity and need of aboriginal Africa for an evolving identity of its own.

Obviously I could write a book of the story of how these changes came about but for the moment I prefer to confine myself to a description of how this world of Portugal in Africa appeared to me when I last visited it just before the storm broke. Both the history of the future and unique character of that world will need some record of that kind one day, if only as a measure of the suddenness, intensity and retrogressive character of the catastrophe that overwhelmed it. But even more, it will need it to understand how this world will have lived on in all that is best in the hearts and minds of the millions of Africans who once knew it so well and for so long.

In case all this sounds too whimsical and fanciful for a world obsessed only with demonstrable appearances, I would point to Brazil. This vast South American country was the first to break politically with metropolitan Portugal, not because of a compulsion to reject the spirit and culture of Portugal but out of an inevitable and typical revulsion against the inadequacies of remote overseas control. Once that was done the culture bonds with Portugal and, in certain significant particulars, with Angola, became more rather than less meaningful. The Angolan bond, the congenital Brazilian nostalgia for the land where all its black people came from as slaves (Cuba, which acquired most of its slaves from Angola as well, shared this nostalgia, which was to become a significant factor in the Cuban interest and success of their invasion of Western Africa), was strong enough in itself to maintain the Portuguese leaven active in the character of Brazil. How did this world appear then, just before the catastrophe which, in the dishonest vocabulary of the social and political scientists of our time, enjoys the euphemism of an "emancipation".

Geographically I had to begin with Angola on the west coast of Africa, because it was fourteen times the size of Metropolitan Portugal and about as big as what we have become accustomed to call "Western Europe". With Mozambique on the east coast added to it the Portuguese possessed nearly 800,000 square miles of the continent, without including Portuguese Guinea, Madeira and the now independent islands of Cape Verde, Sao Tome, and Principe, which, geologically and botanically speaking, are all as much a part of Africa as the British Isles are of Europe. It is true that in this world the numbers of indigenous people of mainly Bantu origin and organised as ever in an extremely varied and complex pattern of tribes, are more thinly spread on the ground than elsewhere in Africa. This is particularly true of Angola which contains less than five million Africans. Yet nowhere else in Africa had the transforming influence of a European culture such deep and tenacious roots. I know that socially, politically and economically this world of Portugal in Africa had for long been more backward and appeared more neglected than the rest of imperial Africa. But there are other significant values in life to consider and happily this is not a book either of sociology or political philosophy to dive into the muddy and troubled water which discussion of decolonisation has become.

These facts are important only in so far as they elucidate the Portuguese contribution to the innate striving of man to transform his way of eating into a meaningful part of his culture. Everywhere else in Africa the results of the European impact may have been far more dramatic and spectacular than in Portuguese Africa. But in its own quiet, unassuming way, the Portuguese presence may have had subtler consequences and proved to have been more lasting than most.

This is due partly to the fact that the Portuguese were the first Europeans in Africa. With an urge that seemed as strange, wasteful, if not downright insane to fifteenth-century Europe as the urge which propels Americans and Russians into outer space appears to many people today, Henry the Navigator forced his captains in their small ships to feel their way south down the coast of Africa so resolutely that by 1483, one Diogo Cao had already set foot in the north of what is now Angola. Three years later Bartholomeo Diaz rounded the Cape of Storms. Eleven years later Vasco de Gama sailed by, to change its name to the Cape of Good Hope, and carried on to the Far East, landing on the way at several places on the coast of Portuguese East Africa, above all on the coral island of Mozambique from which the province derives its present name. By 1505 the Portuguese were established in Mozambique. It was I think a measure of the equality of their influence that while the great empires like those of the far more powerful British, French and Germans vanished many decades ago from Africa, the militarily weak and impoverished people of Portugal stayed far longer. One of the main reasons for this is of real concern to this essentially non-political book on the food of Africa. It was the strange, dogged, undemonstrative belief in themselves and their faith which produced what I still call almost in a nursery way "the going-on-ness" of the Portuguese character and which coloured all they did, even their cooking. There was something traditional about the Portuguese which cancelled out in advance any intimation of doubt that they could ever stop doing something which they had once begun. Wherever they settled, whether it was in Angola, Brazil, Timor or Macao on the coast of China, where they still remain like a little drawing-pin on the vast map of China, they parked themselves and all the belongings that they could carry with them in their cockle-shell ships as if they were going to be there for ever. And until the recent catastrophe they had only been proved wrong once (for I do not count Brazil since there has been no rejection there of the Portuguese inheritance). That happened when Mr. Nehru, who tended to preach the world Sermons on the Mount from a moral Everest of his own presumption, took the lovely Portuguese colony of Goa on the coast of India from the Portuguese by sheer over-whelming military force and against the wishes of the majority of the inhabitants, in the best old fashioned imperial manner.

This "going-on" quality in the Portuguese character was most movingly illustrated for me in my last visit to Baia dos Tigres in the extreme south of Angola. The name means Tiger Bay, which is odd as there are no tigers in Africa, and I can only imagine that in this instance the Portuguese were influenced by the Dutch who mistakenly called leopards, tigers. This in itself is important because in the deeps of history, as we shall see also in cooking, there has been a far greater interchange of culture between the peoples of the Lowlands and the Iberian Peninsula than historians tend to recognise. This interchange indeed has become so taken for granted in the respective national characters of Dutch, Spaniards and Portuguese that they themselves are unaware of it. To someone like myself, however, who has experienced all three cultures, parti-cularly in their colonial extensions, it is clear how important a factor it has been.

As far as Tiger Bay is concerned the deduction is all the more plausible because it is just north of the sandbanks at the mouth of the great Kunena river which divides Angola from South-West Africa. It is a great natural harbour and would no doubt have long since been developed as such if it had not been for the fact that for a long time there was nothing to justify it commercially. There is nothing but the great Kalahari desert behind the bay. It hardly ever rains there. When I was there last I saw enormous thunder-clouds piled high over the bay and the settlement itself, for the moment, an arid island of sand since the sea had severed the headland as it does from time to time. The air below the cloud was so hot and dry that the rain evaporated before it could reach the earth. No trees, fruit or vegetables will grow there except in tubs. The Kalahari sands are driven before the wind over the waves of dunes like spume. All the water, until recently, had to be brought in by sea. Yet for a century a small group of Portuguese fishermen from the Algarve have lived there. They have made it their home. They spend the whole of their lives fishing in the great Antarctic current which runs, broad and deep, north along the western coast. It is full of edible fish of all kinds and such strange phenomena as walrus, seals and even whales, blowing their vapour up into a strangely cold sky where the great white albatross haunts the noonday's darkest blue, like a vision out of "The Ancient Mariner". It has never occurred to these Portuguese fishermen to leave and when I asked them if they hankered to go back to Portugal or even to visit the cities of Angola, they looked at me as if I were mad. They seemed as contented a people as any I have known. I cannot bear the thought of what has happened to them now.

The great captains who began the Portuguese adventure overseas like Vasco da Gama, Albuquerque and Francesco d'Almeida may have been violent, cruel and rapacious as the captains of many nations were in those days, particularly when they were Muslim and Catholic facing what they took to be unbelievers. But the men who carried on were the humble and poor of Portugal, like the fishermen. Their overlords may have been a remote government corrupted by power or merchants jet-propelled by greed, but they themselves as convicts, outcasts or just helpless poor went on wherever they settled as if they were for ever part of Portugal. Some of the noblest figures of all this turbulent history, the greatest and most chivalrous souls, were convicts.

What is most important of all is that the defects of the colonial system to which the indigenous peoples of the Portuguese world in Africa were subjected, were not special defects occurring only in colonies, they were the defects of the social system of Portugal itself. As a result, the psychological and social differences between the poor of Portugal and the Africans were far fewer than those between the Dutch, French and British and their indigenous subjects. This nearness produced from the start an absence of racism and colour prejudice which, ironically enough, exists to this day. I found over and over again that it was utterly impossible to make a Portuguese colour conscious, and convince him that the colour of a man's skin mattered. Only when it came to his faith and culture did the trouble begin. This positive approach above all humanised their defects as well as their virtues and with their gift of "going-on-ness", explained I believe their long presence in the land. Unlike the other empires in Africa too, the feeling of being Portuguese and the will to remain so was reinforced by the Portuguese policy of governing their overseas possessions as integral parts of Metropolitan Portugal—a parallel in some ways of American policy towards Hawaii and Alaska. Indeed so great was this interdependence that the collapse of the mother country inevitably produced a disintegration in Africa which neither the majority of Africans nor the growing number of Portuguese Africans desired.

This interdependence had important consequences in the development of cooking. Perhaps, however, this aspect was not as important as in other parts of Africa we have considered, because indigenous man in the old Portuguese empire had even less to offer than his counterparts elsewhere. His own vague ideas of cooking resembled those of the Bantu of the east. But even more than in east or west, his was largely a pastoral economy. Cattle and sheep were still currency, meat rarely eaten, milk, curds and whey, and farinacious substances, the main diet. This is even stranger in places like the highlands of Angola where perhaps the greatest Bantu cattle-raisers exist. On my last visit among the Cuanhanama in the south, I thought I had never seen anywhere in indigenous Africa so many and such incomparable cattle. I was told that the average tribesman never owned less than a hundred head and was forced to hire herdsmen. The Cuanhanama were such dedicated cattle-men that they would sing special songs for the important moments in the life of their cattle and I have heard them chanting to cows which were bearing calves. Stranger still, they seemed to know a great deal about cattle diseases and how to treat them. My Portuguese companions assured me that they had their own particular cure for the dreaded anthrax, using a potion containing the serum of an animal which had been infected with the same complaint. This seemed to me a startling vindication of the instinctive wisdom of African man since this, after all, is the principle of vaccination.

Yet with all this wealth of cattle, beef was never eaten except, as everywhere else in Bantu Africa, on occasions of overwhelming significance. They had no hesitation in eating the white ibis, the tick-birds which accompanied their cattle everywhere, but for most of the year the cattle remained inviolate. This was clearly a matter of religion. Even when eating tick-birds which were so useful in keeping their cattle free of parasites, they insisted that the birds be boiled in milk. They were afraid disaster might come if they were merely stewed in water.

Their agriculture, like that of their kinsmen in the old Portuguese Africa, was for years of the most primitive kind. One of the mysteries of Africa is why man seems always to have been without cereals and pulses of his own. Sorghums and millet to a limited extent appear to be the only exceptions and he does seem to have grown them for himself long before the coming of the European and Arab. I found Africans, in many parts, making a meal from some cereal which was similar to sorghum, and though it is called massambala in Angola and mapira in Mozambique, it was exactly the same plant. What other vegetables the African needed to supplement his diet, he obtained not by cultivation but by gleaning bush, jungle, highland, plain and desert. In the process he became a remarkable botanist.

It is amazing what he extracted in this way from the savage natural scene. Indeed it is a great pity the European invaders never consulted him properly in this regard, just as, until recently, they remained so profoundly indifferent to his spiritual apprehensions. If the Portuguese and other imperialists who followed them had taken the same interest in what primitive man gleaned from the land as they did in minerals, and had set about developing the indigenous cereals, pulses and fruits, Africa would have made a substantial and startlingly original contribution to the world's food.

Two experiences on my own journey may serve to illustrate this point. One was on the Mozambique side of the Shire highlands, near the frontier of Malawi. There I found Africans harvesting from the bush, in mountain clefts and gorges, what I can only describe as a kind of tree tomato. It is shaped like an unwrinkled passion fruit. It is of the same colour as passion fruit but the skin is thicker. Yet the seeded orange-fruit inside tasted more like a tomato than anything else. It was, I would say, a pagan and unrepentantly savage tomato, fierce and vivid in its flavour; and my imagination was instantly excited by what could be done to so ardent a vegetable with selective cultivation and judicious inter-grafting. It might even rescue the tomato from being the tame, woolly substance of faintly scented water flavoured with sawdust, which it is so often today. I say with some certainty because several of these tree tomatoes, scooped out into the enamel plate of bully beef I had for lunch that day, made even so hackneyed a dish quite memorable. Yet the official who was with me could not even give me its local, let alone botanical name.

A similar thing happened to me a fortnight later in the north of Angola. We encountered some African coffee farmers coming from their allotments in the bush for their noonday meal in the nearby village. They all carried branches thickly clustered with golden fruit that, held as they were on shoulders close to dark, archaic heads, made me think of the golden bough which Anaeas brought back with him from the sacred wood. There were among these branches at least three different kinds of fruit. When I asked if I could be allowed to taste them I was immediately given more fruit than I could hold. All the fruit, particularly on that hot day, was delicious and of a unique savour, cutting through my thirst like a knife. One of them could well have been a member of the mango family and all, if developed by modern scientific means, could become authentic African additions of considerable import to the tables of the world. I asked the officials for the name of the fruit. Again none of them knew either the local or the botanical name.

The explanation is partly rooted in the determination of the Portuguese to be for ever Portugal wherever they go. Yet it is not without an element of paradox because in other parts of the world where the Portuguese established a foothold, as in India, Formosa, China and above all Brazil, they were ready enough to learn all they could from indigenous cultures. The paradox in turn is explained by the fact that in those areas indigenous societies were more highly organised, secure and firmly rooted than those of the Bantu and Negro who so far as imagination, let alone historical research, can stretch, have either been constantly on the march, or from the moment the traffic in slaves started, perpetually on the run.

The result was that the Portuguese imported from lands possessing similar climates and conditions an amazing variety of vegetables they thought Africa could also grow. In this respect their influence on the food and cooking of Africa was most profound of all. This influence stretched far beyond the areas under their control. They were so successful that not only indigenous man but the industrious Dutch imitated them, even claiming, in the end, that they themselves had been the pioneers in this field. Yet it was the brave Portuguese example and initiatives that created the greatest ever revolution in food and eating in Africa.

I have already mentioned how they started the West African fashion of combining meat and fish in one and the same dish, but, in making available to Africa all sorts of new foods the Portuguese example was overwhelming.

I could do no better than let that great eccentric, the unique Sir Harry Johnson, speak of the Portuguese in this matter. Harry Johnson knew his Africa as few others have done. He was not only a great traveller, observer and administrator, but also an artist. He painted and drew the natural African scene in a sensitive, perceptive and affectionate way. Besides, he deserves an honorary mention in any book on the cooking of Africa, because he was such a great lover of food himself. In this regard he appears in the history of the undignified scramble for Africa like a strange, superior sort of Somerset Maugham character.

For instance, long ago I met a very old retired District Commissioner living out his days and his love of Africa near the very *Fort Johnson* named after the singular Sir Harry. He told me that in what is now Malawi, where Harry Johnson did some of his greatest work, he had often encountered him on ulendo, as safari is called in that part of Africa. He was always amazed to see Sir Harry night after night change regularly for dinner in bush and jungle and sit down to his meal at a portable table. The table was always covered with a spotless white cloth, silver cutlery, plates, wine glasses, peaked napkins and all. He would eat while a white-coated Ashanti, champagne in hand, waited on him, indifferent to the lions roaring and leopards coughing in the darkness beyond the ulendo fires.

This is what Sir Harry says: "So early in the history of their African exploration that it is almost the first step they took, the Portuguese brought from China, India and Malacca, the orange tree, the lemon and the lime which besides introducing into Europe —and Europe had hitherto known only the sour wild orange brought by the Arabs—they planted in every part of East and West Africa. From their great possession of Brazil overrun and organised with astounding rapidity they brought to East and West Africa, the

Muscovy duck (which has penetrated far into the interior of Africa, if indeed it has not crossed the continent), chillies, peppers, maize, tobacco, the tomato, pineapple, sweet potato, manioc from which tapioca is made, and other less known forms of vegetable food. The Portuguese also introduced the domestic pig into Africa and on the west coast the domestic cat, possibly also certain breeds of dogs. The Englishman has brought with him the potato and has introduced into most of the colonies the horse, and in places improved breeds of cattle, sheep and goats, a good many European vegetables and fruit trees, the tea plant, the coffee plant (which has, however, only been transported from other parts of Africa) and many shrubs and trees of special economic value. But what are these introductions —almost entirely for his own use—compared in value with the vast bounty of the Portuguese?"

He should have added that they also brought the banana. But there we have it: it was the Portuguese, gardeners at heart, with their capacity to endure against all the odds—the history of the early colonists makes almost unbearable reading—that forced an entire continent into a new range of cooking.

While on this subject, it is as well to emphasise that in the process the Portuguese created, as it were, two wings of cooking in Africa, held together by the main body of their presence. Roughly, one is South American, or more specifically Brazilian, and is most evident in Angola. The other is a compound effect, in Mozambique, of the Portuguese experiences of the East from its Arabian outposts in Zanzibar to the coast of Malabar in India and Malacca on to the Celestial Empire. Since there was a constant coming and going between Angola and Mozambique from the earliest days, these two schools naturally borrowed freely from one another. Yet it is surprising that they retain nuances of their own. Rice, spice and the fruits of the Orient feature more prominently in Mozambique than they do in Angola. I have often as a matter of course been offered curry in Mozambique, never in Angola. There are still restaurants serving only Arab food in Mozambique. On my last visit there, in fact, I had the same rice I first ate in the Sultan's Palace in Zanzibar, over forty years ago. But in Angola, from the very beginning, relations with Brazil were very special and very close, closer even than those between it and Portugal.

Life in the capital outpost, Saint Paul de Luanda, as it was originally called, was for centuries like that of a Brazilian city. The cooking in town was Brazilian, the foods seasoned with South American condiments, and there was a way of doing chicken called "Muamba", which had as great a claim to being the national dish of Angola as any. It is purely Brazilian origin. A Brazilian dialect was spoken in preference to the Portuguese of Cintra and it is said that Angolan ladies were thoroughly Brazilian in their "ostentation and indolence". Both they and their men, even when they were in colourful rags as they often were, moved everywhere accompanied by a mass of slaves. Indeed it was slaves and slavery on which the whole society was founded because Luanda was the main base for the Portuguese traffic and Angola the main source of supply for the traders. They culled Angola for the best of the indigenous population; and caused the great scarcity of manpower which afflicts the country to this day. Yet despite all this, a sort of dream-memory of Angola haunts the imagination of Brazil and inspires its poets and musicians to sing of it as a sort of African Hesperides in which their ancestors once knew an age of gold. When I was last in Angola I listened to a young Brazilian pop singer on the radio exhalting Angola to screaming adolescent audiences in precisely this manner. The memory of Brazil may have been somewhat blurred in Angola even then because, with the coming of the aeroplane and the steamship, Portugal had asserted itself in a much more masterful way and was pouring new Portuguese colonists into the land. Yet a similar yearning for Brazil remains. Consciously or unconsciously it is there in the deeps of the mind as it is visibly in the fruits of the earth.

Mozambique had its share of the slave trade as well, though it was on a much smaller scale. The trade seems to have been dominated by the Arabs from Zanzibar who freely raided southward into the Portuguese territories right down to Lake Malawi until Harry Johnson removed the last traces of Arab power there towards the end of the last century. Colonisation was never encouraged in Mozambique as it was in Angola. Mozambique was the fortified gateway, a series of strong points, on the way to the East. The Portuguese never had any intention of settling in it and their officials and merchants came and went as soon as they had completed their term of office or taken their profit, leaving a rapidly growing Mulatto population to maintain a constant and continuing thread of Portuguese "being" in East Africa.

The gateway to the Portuguese world of Africa itself, however, has never been for me either Angola or Mozambique but the island of Madeira. However close it is to Lisbon and the north-west coast of Africa, this island is the first outpost both of land and man in the African world which Renaissance man discovered.

Madeira itself is one of a group of three islands set in the Atlantic like points at the apex of an isosceles triangle. The northernmost is called Santos, the easternmost Desertas, and the southern and principal one, Madeira. Somewhere in the great deeps of the sea which divides Madeira from Santos, runs a mysterious demarcation line which decisively divides the world of the Mediterranean from that of Africa. It was and is a fateful demaraction line in the mind of Mediterranean man. Santos is an island of sun, sand and low dune-like hills with curved yellow beaches. Geologically and botanically it belongs to the Sahara and what I called at the beginning, Mediterranean Africa. Madeira, only a few miles across a dark blue strait, is a mountain complex, a giant sort of cinder thrown straight out of the volcanic system of Africa which still acts so powerfully in the Great Rift and reaches through earth and ocean as far out as the Azores.

It is a mountain moreover which often has its head in cloud and swirling mists and vapours. When Henry the Navigator's sailors first reached Santos and saw the mountain, flying cloud and mist like storm signals from its head, they were afraid to go on. For all the Navigator's urging to the contrary, they still believed that the world had an edge to it and that if one travelled far enough across the seas one would sail over its edge and drop into a fathomless abyss. This mountain of Madeira, they feared, marked the end of the world and they paused for many months at Santos before crossing the narrow strait over to the main island. The records of their voyage say that the whole of the mountain and its foothills were covered in a dense orchid-filled forest that came right down to the edge of the sea. It must have been one of the most beautiful and innocent sights ever seen by man since his expulsion from the Garden at his own beginning, but in their haste to make clearings in the forest for settlement, the Portuguese set the forest alight. The fire got out of control and, historians tell us, it burned, like a torch held high over the ocean, for six years. Yet so fertile is the volcanic soil, so skilled are the Portuguese as gardeners that in time the island was resurrected in a singular new beauty of plants, trees and flowers, all purified by fire. By some miracle, many of the original flowers and plants had survived to prove, even more than the rocks, how much a part of Africa Madeira is.

There is the freesia for instance. It grows wild in Madeira as it does elsewhere in Africa. Its existence for me is a touching demonstration of how so giant a continent as Africa can use the strength which hurls Kilimanjaro 20,000 feet into the air to produce a flower of the unique, delicate and tender scent of the freesia. I except that is why the freesia is for me the heraldic badge of all that Africa, in the fullness of time, is meant to become. I have met its scent at dawn in the Huri hills on the frontiers of Ethiopia when I had no previous intimation of its existence—and been moved beyond measure by its evocations of the sweetness and tenderness brought out by its true strength.

On my first journey to England as a boy, I arrived at Madeira one tranquil, cloudless evening, when the sky was like a comb of honey. After days of sailing over a blank sea, shining as a buckler of steel, I stared with amazement at this green and dramatic little world carved, in colourful terraces, into the emerald flanks of the great mountain and its foothills. Yet different as it was from anything I had left behind thousands of miles away in the Cape of Good Hope, it did not make a foreign impact on my senses. Such differences as there were, I felt intuitively, were differences within the African family. Such a response seemed utterly absurd and irrelevant at the time. I could not explain it to myself until I began to associate it with a subtle perfume reaching out like a benediction from the land. I suddenly realised it was the scent of freesias. All was clear. Freesias grow profusely on my own farm on the Orange River thousands of miles away to the south. They are the first to flower in the spring. When the dew falls at night, their scent pervades the air to such an extent that my ancestors called them "evening flowers". I associate many countries with a particular scent—Zanzibar with cloves, Sumatra with the dank odour of mangrove, jungle and palm; the Straits of Malacca with all-pervasive spices and so on. But the island of Madeira is the only island I associate with the smell of flowers, the scent of freesias. It is for me, a frontier. Whenever it vanishes behind me as I leave Madeira, northward-bound, I know that I have crossed from Africa into the classical Western Ocean, the "Sea of Darkness" as the old Portuguese sailors called it. The moment I pick up the scent going south, I know I am home.

This island door-step to Africa was perfectly equipped to become a kind of botanical kindergarten for instructing the Portuguese into what they should do agriculturally on the mainland of Africa. The mountain and the complex of deep valleys and steep gorges which time, wind and the wild Atlantic carved out dramatically between it and its foothills, provided it with the climates and conditions of all the latitudes of the world. In fact, botanically speaking, it is a model in miniature of the globe itself. Almost everything can be grown in Madeira, as the Portuguese quickly found. They transplanted to it not only all the crops of their own part of Europe but also those of the great new world they discovered beyond. But, what is perhaps more important, is that at Madeira a new kind of Portuguese came into being who, without turning his back on Portugal, was born with the instinct to look out to the new world beyond. It is no accident that Columbus lived on the island for nearly a decade before he went back to ask Isabella of Spain to finance his voyage of discovery. To this day, the hardy, pertinacious, impoverished and yet gentle people of what is now an over-populated island, remain in the forefront of Portuguese expansion overseas. They appear today in increasing numbers even in South Africa as the most successful market gardeners. Above all they provoded a steady stream of reinforcements for the settlements in Africa, particularly in Angola.

The food of the islanders unfortunately is not readily available to outsiders except in the bewildering variety of fruit they grow. The hotels, as is to be expected in an island economy which depends greatly on tourists, go in for international cuisine. I must hasten to add that in an hotel like Reid's which has always been a cardinal ingredient traveller's lore, like Shephard's in Cairo, or Raffles in Singapore, the food is as good as any to be had in the world. The officials of the island who come and go between it and Portugal may eat much in the way they do at home. But the islanders themselves have interesting variants of their own, cooked according to family recipes treated like articles of faith of a kitchen bible, not lightly to be shared with strangers.

One of their greatest delicacies is a strange kind of eel-like fish called the "espada", almost as old as the prehistoric ceoleocanth. The taste of this fish, bringing to the modern table as it does one of the oldest savours of the ocean, is as unique as the way of catching it. The espada lives a mile down in waters where the pressures are so great that very often when it is dragged to the surface it bursts. It is always fished for at night and one of the most characteristic spectacles of Madeira is the lights of the fishermen at work, waving like lanterns over the ocean as their tiny boats ride the waves. Their hooks are baited with bits of octopus, and, so far down do they sink their lines, that it takes them as long as two hours to haul up the espada once they have caught it.

The espada is prepared for the table, of course, in all the ways that fish can be done. Fresh, it is delicious fried in a light batter or breadcrumbs. It is as good braised and covered with a sauce made of the tomatoes the island grow so well, flavoured with a touch of garlic and onion. It is served in the homes of the middle classes too with a sauce made from one of the wines of Madeira, and then it is a dish beyond compare.

Besides the espada, some three hundred other kinds of fish of all colours and shapes are caught off the island. The fish market is one of the most astonishing and colourful I know and is patronised by some of the most exacting shoppers in the world. As one exasperated fisherman once explained: "You would think they were buying horses and not fish because they even inspect the teeth of the fish to see how old they are."

Meat is scarce but the favourite, as in many other parts of Portugal, is pork. They have many ways of cooking it that are important because they became the established ways of doing both pork and its equivalents, like wild pig and warthog in Angola and Mozambique. The meat seldom goes direct to saucepan or oven but is subjected to some form of marinating. One favourite marinade, used as much in Madeira as it is in Mozambique, consists basically of dry Madeira and wine vinegar combined in equal proportions. Salt, pepper, pounded garlic, cloves, sweet red peppers and bay leaf are added and the pork steaks are cut with a good fringe of lard, and are left to soak in the marinade for eight hours. The steaks are then cut in cubes and simmered for a while in the marinade. They are then drained and fried until brown, great care being taken to see that they do not stick to the saucepan. This is why the original fringe of fat is so important because the success of the dish depends on the meat frying in its own fat. Just before serving, a generous amount of fresh orange juice, laced with dry Madeira, is poured over the meat.

In Mozambique I found that instead of adding potatoes or bread

to the pork, normally the meat was cooked by itself in the prescribed manner and served with rice done in various ways that can
be more closely examined when I discuss the food in the eastern
wing of the Portuguese world of Africa. Even I, who am not a pork
addict, found this dish delicious, particularly with rice. I enjoy too
the Madeira way of doing chickens with a stuffing of grapes. They
continually baste the chicken with olive oil until it is dark brown
and crisp and finish it off with some fresh lime or orange juice
poured over it to join the natural gravy.

Finally, there are the cakes and biscuits of the island. Like the
people of Metropolitan Portugal, the Portuguese of Madeira and of
Africa love sweet things. They have a special genius for combining
a bewildering variety of ingredients into one small dark brown
biscuit or one monumental cake. Then there are the so-called
honey-cakes and cinnamon-biscuits always ready to be offered to
a visitor with a glass of Madeira.

The island's greatest contribution to the world's cooking is its
wine. It was for long the farthest south that the European vine had
ever penetrated. The first cuttings appear to have come from Cyprus
before other varieties were added from Portugal and even the
Rhineland. But whatever the origin, the ancient character of Africa,
preserved in the earth and volcanic rock, so transformed the grape
that it acquired a unique and distinct identity of its own. It produced, moreover, the first wine of Africa and its successor on the
island, resounding all over the merging modern world, encouraged
the Dutch two centuries later to establish the great vineyards of the
Cape of Good Hope.

It is to my mind a great wine to drink for its own sake as the
eighteenth-century British and Americans knew so well. The British
even evolved a special cake called Madeira to eat with it after church
on Sundays—the cake has nothing to do with the island! The
plantation founders in the southern states of America liked it so
well that, in a wild and woolly Western (the only book in English
I could find in Conakry on the west coast of Africa) I read of a
villainous rancher who offered it to the cowboy hero with the
words: "Have some Madeira. America was built on it. Washington
drank it, Jefferson gulped it down and the plantation owners
imported it as freely as they imported slaves."

However, I must mention it also because I believe it is the greatest
cooking wine of the world and, were it not so expensive, would be

used very widely. Moreover, I believe the limits of its range of gastronomic usefulness have not yet been reached, especially in the cooking of wild fowl and game and the making of sweets. It is both subtle and strong, tender and stern, in a gamut stretching from honeyed Malmseys to dry Sercials. It can, in its sweet form, be used with a touch of dark brown sugar and cinnamon to serve with peeled avocados without impairing the delicate flavour or, as the people of old Portuguese Africa use it, to go with a sort of angel's food made of pomegranate grains, diced avocado, and seeded and chopped up custard apples. The ways in which it is used in European cooking, from making anything from sauce Bigarade— Madeira has its own recipe for this as well—to the classical English trifle where it is more successful, to my taste, than the traditional sherry, are almost without end. Where it is sovereign in its dominion is in the preparation of wild fowl and game. It has a strength which no other wine possesses to civilise the wild, vivid, savage nature of African meat. This is so because, since it is itself of the aboriginal soil of Africa, there is a natural affinity between it and the animal world. Madeira is one of the longest-lived wines, but, old as a wine may be, its own special history is never forgotten and the vanished people who made it are remembered. I have a bottle which I bought in the island some time ago. It is a Verdelho of the year 1862 made by one Joao Pereira de Oliveira in the district of Sao Martinho. There were only five bottles left. I have also a Reserve Campanario which was produced by D. Maria Favilha Vieria in 1846. It is the last bottle in existence. I have a Grabham Sercial of 1818 and obtained it with this note: "Dr. Michael Grabham, who married Miss Mary Anne Blandy, inherited through his wife a very fine cellar. This he left to his son, Walter Grabham. Walter, who died in 1955, left the cellar to his cousins, Graham and John Blandy. This bottle of wine formed part of that wonderful collection and there are only two bottles left." So far I have not found an occasion important enough to give me the courage to open any of these bottles because I have the awesome feeling that in drinking them I would be destroying a living manifestation of history itself, rather like an unimaginative hunter shooting, for sheer sensation, the last surviving specimen of a rare species of animal.

But perhaps all that Madeira, its people, its food and its wine mean in the making of the Portuguese world of Africa, can be focused, as under a microscope, in an experience of my own. One of my oldest friends lives in Madeira. He is a member of an unique and distinguished English family who, more than any single group, has helped to make the modern Madeira. They have been in the island for some two centuries now. They have remained very English and yet are as committed to the life and history of the island as any of the Portuguese inhabitants. The children may go to school and university in England but they are born in Madeira, live and die there and in the course of time have provided a clear British thread to be woven into the stout cord of Portuguese continuity. For years, on more voyages than I can remember between the Cape of Good Hope and Southampton, I have been a constant visitor in their homes. I have spent many a holiday with them on the island and I have never walked through the door of the family home without immediately being aware of how the past, from that far moment when Madeira was just a torch of fire in the darkness over the western ocean, is still a living and creative element in the present. Not only the conversation, but the inanimate objects in the fortress-like house seem to become animate and eloquent to the eye and to heighten one's perception of the meaning of history. I think of the paintings for instance, such as the one of a naval engagement presented by a grateful Nelson to an ancestor; or the heavy cut glass decanters with their broad bases made to prevent them from toppling over in the cuddies of the tossing East Indiamen from which they were originally purchased; or the plate, once the proudest exhibit in the dining saloon of a smart China clipper.

I have sat down for dinner on many a bland evening, watching the day decline through broad windows, seeing the white light broken up in all its rainbow colours until the brown of evening took over, while the heights of Funchal became strung with garlands of light. The night always seemed to me to step up out of the East, where Africa lay near, in one swift colossal stride and to stand tall, firm and proud over the island in a manner which was unmistakable —that of a sort of High Commissioner of the Africa whose speciality is night, and, at night more even than in the day, claims the island as one of its own.

We would talk over a superbly cooked dinner round a table with a bowl full of the jewelled fruit of Madeira, in a room filled with flowers and their scent. The conversation would move like a shuttle in and out of remote past and urgent present, taking up threads and weaving them, as it were, into a single twist of meaning. The last time I dined there I remember we had a long conversation about a member of the family who, that very day, looking for a contract in the archives of the family, had discovered an account submitted to the Belgian Government for supplying Stanley with the cooks, mules and muleteers for one of his fateful excursions into the Congo. This led to a long catalogue of the contributions made by the family to the development of Africa.

We talked of how an American admiral one day anchored his training ship in the bay of Funchal. In the fashion of the day he was allowed to travel with his own family and he had two lovely daughters with him. One of the daughters married my host's father. I knew her myself and saw for myself the dynamic centre she became for all that was progressive in the life of the island. And so on up to the present, to the day when Winston Churchill came to recuperate from the strains of the last war. He was perturbed at first when, on his way to Reid's hotel, driving through the crowded streets of Funchal, not a cheer was raised. He saw nothing but crowd upon crowd of solemn faces staring silent as he drove by. He must have thought it a sign of hostility or at least indifference, for my host, who was with him, tells me that when it was explained to him that this was the ultimate Madeira way of showing their most profound respect, the tears came to his eyes.

But it was the story of the wine we were drinking that, more than anything else, put the occasion in its proper frame of living history. The wine came from the supreme vintage of 1789, the year the Bastille was stormed. The British Government thought it good enough for an Emperor. They bought it from my host's ancestors and stocked Napoleon's cellars at Longwood on St. Helena with it. When Napoleon died, the family, knowing how good it was, bought the wine back from the British Government. What made the wine even more awesome to drink was the fact that it cannot even be simulated today. The species of grape from which it was produced was subsequently eliminated by disease and the vineyards of Madeira had to be restocked with vines brought from California. I know of no other place in Africa which can provide a comparable experience of food and wine in so continuous and continuing a context of history and civilisation.

After Madeira, the progression of history leads one to Angola. I went to Angola twice before the war. I have paid four visits since, the second just after the catastrophic insurrection in the northernmost province of Uige. Some 30,000 Portuguese and African workers, employed mostly by African coffee growers in the area, were massacred because they did not belong to the same tribe as the invaders. The future of the Portuguese presence seemed then in grave doubt and I remember leaving the country wondering whether a collapse on the Congo scale was imminent.

I was there for the third time only a few years ago and I hardly recognised the country. The doubt had gone. The country was transformed into a dynamic modern economy. Even oil had been found, and was being discovered in increasing quantities over an ever wider area. Broad roads had been built where there had been no roads before. A policy of settlement by immigrants from Madeira and Portugal was being zealously pursued. For centuries Angola had been little more than a coast of ports linked to fortified outposts with tenuous trading connexions into the interior. On my last visit, it looked one of the most purposeful parts of the whole of Africa. No area of Africa had changed so dramatically in my own lifetime. Even so, only a small fraction of Angola's ultimate potential had been realised. For its size and natural resources it had one of the smallest populations per square mile in Africa; as a Portuguese statistician despairingly put it, writing about one of the most promising districts of Angola: "There is only half an inhabitant per square kilometre."

It still has the greatest reserves of unused terrain in the whole continent. It combines within itself almost all that Africa has to offer of minerals, plants, animals and climate. In the north it touches on West Africa but, away from a narrow coastal belt, it soars rapidly up, in a series of vast, plateau-like terraces, into highlands of great beauty where anything can be grown.

The progress I found in Angola was reflected in the food of the "new old Portuguese" as I called them, as well as of the indigenous inhabitants. There were obviously remote and vast areas where men still tended to live as they always had. Milk from cows and goats remained the basic diet along with the local variety of funge. Funge is Africa's substitute for bread, an old friend encountered from the Sahara to the Kalahari, the Angolan version of the cassawa or other flour porridges of Negro Africa, the "posho" of East Africa, or the mealie meal of Zululand. It is made by cooking the maize flour, manioc or millet into a porridge thick enough to be eaten with the fingers.

I noticed on that journey in the remote interior that smoked fish, imported from the great and expanding fisheries on the coast, was being eaten more than ever before. I felt more changes were on the way as in a country which believed in making every man work whether he liked it or not, there was hardly a grown man in the interior who had not experienced a westernised form of diet on plantations, and in the industrial towns, and brought back new tastes and appetites to his native village. Funge was being increasingly threatened by a taste for bread and the Portuguese everywhere make excellent bread. Indeed I was amazed to find, even in the smallest outpost, how the air in the early morning would be filled with the wonderful smell of bread extracted at dawn from the oven of some small bakery, inn or merchant household and how one would automatically be served with rolls still warm from the baking. Eaten with delicious Angola coffee I would not have exchanged them for a croissant in Paris.

Even the indigenous drinks, with their deep roots in tribal tradition, were losing their popularity. "Matete", which is a kind of gruel made of cooked flour and water was a sort of national drink of Angola. Fifteen years ago it was still drunk by African workers in the cities. But, on my last journey, I had to go far into the interior to see the tribesmen gulping it down at breakfast, while their wives prepared the morning funge. Yet even there the mark of change was upon the scene for I saw the wives making the sign of the cross over the flour before stirring it with a wooden spoon. The sign was often repeated by their men as they rolled the funge into a ball between their fingers before swallowing it. The potent wines made from palms and bananas that used to be offered to guests on special occasions were much rarer. More and more, the good honest peasant wine of Portugal, as well as coffee, was taking over.

The greatest changes of all, however, were among the Portuguese themselves and were most obvious in the cities and settlements. I must concentrate on these, for the evolution of cooking depends mainly on them. Ten years ago the food, even in the best of hotels and restaurants in the capital, was mediocre. One always ate well in the homes of high officials or rich merchants, but nowhere else. Just before Independence, however, it was different. Almost everywhere one went there were hotels or inns that served the traveller well. This was due both to the increase of Portuguese still committed to living in Angola, as well as to a new kind of administration.

The men who were trained for modern administration in the early and most creative days of the Salazar régime, before the war, started to appear everywhere in positions of command. The numbers of Portuguese who freely came to Angola to make it their only home had increased a thousandfold.

Many of them were young men who first knew the country as conscripts sent out to battle with insurrection and rebellion and found, on their return to Portugal, that they had fallen in love with Angola. In the far interior, in the highlands above Nova Lisboa, for instance, I met a young Portuguese, a graduate of the university Coimbra, who was starting up a newspaper of his own. When I asked him why, he said simply: "When I went back from the war to Portugal I found I was no longer happy to be just a civilised man. Africa had made me into something different: half Portuguese, half African—half civilised, half primitive, and I thought I could make the two into one only by coming to live in Angola." He practised so much what he preached that he married an African girl, and, to illustrate the complete absence of racism and colour prejudice of the Portuguese, I should add that they were both among the guests invited to a banquet the Governor gave for me with the generous sense of hospitality so natural to the Portuguese towards the stranger in those days.

In the home of this couple I ate food which owed as much to Africa as it did to Portugal. I remember a noonday meal of prawns done mainly with coconut. I should emphasise that one indication of the wide natural range of food available in Angola is that fresh water shrimps and prawns are almost as abundant in the rivers of the interior as in the estuaries on the coast. These prawns had been caught by African fishermen in the great river nearby. They had been browned first in a mixture of butter and olive oil—it is significant that the olive tree has found its way from Portugal to Angola—and mixed with diced onions. When brown, they had been mixed with coconut milk, some fresh tomato purée, some chopped red chillies, pepper and ginger and slowly simmered until done. Meanwhile, the meat of the coconut shell had been well pounded in a mortar, salted and piled in a plate covered with parsley and lettuce. The shrimp mixture, two minutes before serving, was laced with a glass of dry Madeira, and then, when it was ready, was poured over the coconut meat and served with rice.

In the same house I ate a superb chicken dish in the Muamba

manner so popular in Angola. The chicken was cut up and cooked with some cloves of garlic, onion, hot red peppers, pumpkin and sweet potato leaves. The secret of cooking this dish, I gathered from my hostess, was to cook it very slowly on a low heat so that the liquid of the pumpkin could be slowly extracted to stew the sweet potato leaves, and help blend it with all the other ingredients into a whole.

We finished the meal with coffee. I never realised how good Angola coffee was until that evening. We had a long discussion about coffee—the various ways of growing it, of preparing the beans so they give of their best and of making a brew which extracts the full savour. I had not realised before how seriously the Portuguese in Africa took coffee or how well they grew it. My ignorance was all the more inexcusable because I thought I knew rather a lot about the matter, since one of my greatest friends once helped to grow what is perhaps the greatest coffee in all the world: San Vicente. San Vicente and the "Blue Mountain" varieties have always been such close contenders for the world championship title that it is a matter of personal taste which comes first. But that it is one or the other, no person fully initiated to the inner mystery of coffee drinking before the war ever doubted. Through this friend, over the years, I had a glimpse into all the labyrinthine nuances of the coffee cult. I have my own preferences but it never occurred to me that suddenly, in the far north in the interior of Angola, I would discover a coffee whose flavour rivals the best. I thought at first the secret must be in the making and accordingly asked my hostess how it was done. Her reply shook my imagination even more. The beans were first sugared, roasted and ground fresh, in the universally prescribed manner, so it was evidently not the preparation. It was the fact that the ground coffee, approximately a tablespoonful for every cup, was put in a muslin bag and suspended from the rim of a very ordinary enamel coffee pot, reaching one-third of the way down inside. Freshly boiled water—and this she stressed was most important, the water had to be used the moment it boiled, otherwise it became spoilt—was slowly poured straight into the pot until it was two-thirds full. The pot was then stood on a low heat and the strained liquid poured into cups and passed through the muslin bag again some half a dozen times or more without the liquid ever again being allowed to boil. The heat was so adjusted that the liquid remained just off the boil. The result was triumphant but the cause of my amazement was not this; it was because the manner was precisely the same we have always followed when preparing our coffee in the interior of South Africa. I had thought of it as a purely South African method but now I had to accept that, in its small way, it was an eloquent testimony how much we in Africa owe, in our ways of eating, to the Portuguese. It was another example of the forgotten interchange of cultures.

So seriously did the Portuguese take their coffee—it applied as much to Mozambique as Angola—that they told me they judged hotels, restaurants and the quality of a wife's housekeeping by the coffee served to guests. All this was very much in my mind when I went to the great coffee plantations of Uige in the north. They were among the most beautiful I had ever seen. The forests in which they grew—because the best coffee must have shade—gave one the feeling of being in some kind of coffee cathedral, so tall and solemn were the trees. I would enter a plantation straight from the white heat of the tropical day and walk down long aisles between the tall pillars of trees, throwing Gothic arches of shade over a vast congregation of coffee bushes, branches bowed reverently with the weight of berries upon them. I thought that perhaps all this efficiency, order and creative cultivation of Uige was exceptional but later I saw the same phenomenon in other great coffee areas.

All this I should have anticipated because, after all, I knew that coffee was a native of Africa, and had long been familiar with the claim that it came originally from Kaffa in the far north of Ethiopia. Coffee should therefore be as at home in the soil of Angola as anywhere else in Africa. When I told this to the dynamic Portuguese coffee expert who was guiding me around, he remarked: "The story is even more astonishing than you think. All the coffee bushes in Angola, Brazil and the Far East are the descendants of just two beans of the species *coffee Arabica* taken from Ethiopia and planted in the botanical gardens of Paris. From the berries of these two bushes came all the coffee plantations of the modern world." But no other plantation provided a berry with quite such a wild, vivid, rhapsodic gypsy taste as here in Africa.

In the coffee plantations of Uige too, I had a glimpse of how the African worker was fed by European employers. Breakfast was millet funge and smoked dried fish fried in palm oil. At the end of the day, they ate a stew of meat and yellow rice with a ration of red wine. I cannot pretend that the conditions in which they lived and the immense gap between them and the standards of their employers was to my liking. Wherever I go in Africa—in the new Africa governed by Africans as well as the old—this gulf between the African poor and their employers weighs heavily on me. One would have thought the elementary lessons of history would prevent anyone in these days from allowing so great a divide in human society. All I can say, in fairness, is that it was a problem not peculiar to the Portuguese and that there were more compensations for these inadequacies in their system than in other parts of the continent. However, I mention it not to make moral point of my own but merely to show how even so humble a diet is an immense stride forward from the kind of cooking one finds in the remote primitive areas of the land.

I remember, too, a noonday dinner with the energetic Governor of Uige who was well aware of the urgency of bringing the bulk of the population of Angola into the contemporary world. He lived not in a palace in Carmona but in an unpretentious, although comfortable, villa, unguarded and open to all sorts of informal callers throughout the day. I remember the food we ate for three main reasons. We began again with prawns, and it was on this occasion I realised how shellfish-conscious the Portuguese are. The prawns on this occasion had been flown in from the sea and were a good deal bigger and fleshier than those I had eaten from the river. They had been grilled on thin bamboo skewers over a charcoal fire while being basted with a sauce of oil flavoured with chopped garlic, lemon, salt and crushed peppers. The drippings had been carefully garnered and made into a sauce which accompanied the prawns. This was followed by the main dish of pork done in a variant of the Madeira manner I have described. Pork was the only meat of the old Portuguese Africa that can be compared with its equivalent in British Africa. The Portuguese may have excelled as fishermen, gardeners and specialist cultivators but they never equalled the British in animal husbandry. On the whole the meat of Portuguese Africa was inferior and best braised in a casserole or used as an ingredient in their fantastic hotpots.

The pork was, as to be expected, delicious but what made it exceptional was its accompanying dish of yellow rice. I gathered that this was prepared by being browned first in olive oil and then cooked in a thick, cast-iron frying-pan with saffron and a stock made from the blood of the animal. Such use of blood, I discovered was common all over the old Portuguese Africa. Whether it was chicken, mutton, goat, pork or beef, the blood was never allowed to run to waste but used either in sauces, gravies, soups or as direct ingredients of casseroles and stews.

The pork was followed by a salad of lettuce and tomatoes with a dressing of olive oil from the south of Angola and lemon juice produced locally. The use of the lemon was unusual. Wine vinegar from Portugal is the normal ingredient and the making of the salad dressing taken almost as seriously as coffee. I listened to many an argument over what was the best way. The point was illustrated for me by the Governor who told me that they had a proverb in Angola which illustrated the importance of the matter. "We say," he said, "that to make a good salad dressing it takes a miser to decide the proportion of vinegar, a prodigal that of the oil, a sage to determine the quantity of salt, and a madman to beat up the whole lot together."

The meal ended with large slices of fresh pineapple covered in the juice of a grenadillas and pressed-out pomegranate seeds, sweetened with brown Angola sugar, a touch of cinnamon and a dash of port.

I wish I had the space to go into all the variations of Angolan food offered to me in the detail of their own particular setting because until that particular journey I had not realised the extent to which the two are interdependent. I found, looking back, that food and place were like Siamese twins of memory. For instance, there was Dondo in the interior, founded in 1625 and once the centre of a great trade fair for all coffee, palm oil, peanuts, rubber, ivory and hides from the abundant Malange area and beyond. It had all the quintessentials of a little Portuguese city. The Portuguese concept of a city presupposes a square, public gardens and flowers, and Dondo had all these, with dazzling beds, a little bandstand in the centre and faded seventeenth-century houses increasingly threatened by garish contemporary constructions. I think of it and remember at once a good, sound honest dish I ate there of mutton, pot roasted and finished off in a sauce of the sheep's own blood, served with a white rice spotted with red pimentos, chopped and cooked in butter.

I think of Nova Lisboa which was once destined to be a new capital and already had a population of some 80,000, impressive, solidly built homes, swimming pools, streets, avenues of trees, a university, and was cleaner than any other town in Africa except perhaps Lourenço Marques—now Móputo. I remember thinking I had never seen any town in the world with so many umbrellas because almost every afternoon the rain came down so regularly that one could set one's watch by it. The sun would come out after the rain and set the landscape steaming, but the night would be cool and damp. How grateful I was then for the most complex hotpot I have ever eaten. It contained meat, susages made with blood, bacon, chicken, sweet potatoes, courgettes, potatoes, carrots, cabbage, mange-tout beans and was dished up with a fluffy pimento rice and a thick, white lemon sauce to cover it.

Luanda, the capital, was memorable for many dishes but above all the finest chicken Muamba I had ever eaten. I had it in the dining-room of my hotel, the Continental, and artichocke leaves had been used in it instead of the sweet potato leaves of the similar dish I had in the far interior. Instead of starting with melon, in Luanda, I would begin my dinners with papaya because the papayas were not only the biggest I have ever seen in Africa but the flavour of the fruit was of the most delicate sweetness. I would eat it with the juice of Angola lime, sugared with a few drops of port, unusual for my puritan palate, since I like my fruit, even strawberries and raspberries, pure, without sugar or cream.

Mossamades, in the extreme south, on the edge of the Kalahari desert, was a surprisingly Portuguese little city. Despite its arid climate it had sheltered little gardens growing fruit, vegetables, papaya trees, and streets lined with tamarisk and palm that, at certain times of the day, made one think of the Algarve. Here, by a sea invaded on a broad front by the cold Antarctic current, the air was cool and the choice of fish truly bewildering. Fish I had thought purely South African appeared regularly, often with a thick tomato and onion sauce flavoured with garlic and peppers, but above all uplifted by the sharp angular flavour of tomato.

There was also the neat little village of Lena near Luso on the Benguella railway, where I saw as many lemons as I had ever seen in Italy, but which I remember above all for the wonderful tiger-fish caught in the nearby Zambezi river. I had it served grilled on charcoal, scales and all, with a pungent sauce of tomatoes, oil, garlic and peppers, so that none of its savour was lost and the militant nature of the fish was preserved. There was another fish too, popular among the nearby Luena people, who were among the wealthiest of the

Bantu of the interior. They were the tuquais, trapped in their thousands in the tributaries of the Zambezi, split open, dried in the sun and although of an unsavoury odour, a great Bantu delicacy, exported by the ton to the capital and other cities on the coast. Another large fish found in the lakes and rivers of Carmeia, was not unlike a barbel. It was often a good five feet long, with a moustache like that of an Edwardian sergeant-major, pointed and glistening with *pommade Hongroise*. It is the only pedestrian fish I know because it is said to be able to live for some time out of the water and to move, by a process of judicious jerks, long distances from river to river. Barbecued, they were a welcome variant to hackneyed camping food.

But most touching of all for me was the town of Sao de Baindera in the melodramatically beautiful highlands in the south of Angola where the escarpments rise straight out of the sands, close to the desert-beleaguered city of Mossamedes. Here was a sort of African Madeira but in a far greater setting. The whole area was developed nearly a century ago by people from the island. They came, poor, ill-equipped to begin life in Africa, in grass huts, their high horizon made higher still by the soaring Chela mountains. They built irrigation channels in strict Euclidean patterns, certain that one day they would also have a town with a great square and garden at its heart. They planted the vegetables, the fruit trees and the flowers and in time created gardens that were copies of those left behind. They brought their pigs with them, their own cattle and built enclosures to protect them from lions and leopards. They even sent back to Madeira for an image of the Virgin so that in a cleft of a rock nearby, which clearly resembled one of the foothills of their island, they could have a shrine to which they could make the pilgrimages that seem as vital to the people of Madeira as a walk-about to the aborigines of the Never-Never in Australia. One still saw carts, drawn by the same oxen as in Madeira, pass by houses surrounded by geraniums and carnations. On feast days one would find a band playing in the square and people swimming in one of the most beautiful swimming pools in the world, a natural lake, surrounded with terraces of flowers and trees. The odds had been all against their succeeding but there it was, a thriving city surrounded with green settlements. One looked down on them with amazement from the heights of Porta do Bango because they were such convincing and tender evidence of civilisation. Yet when one turned to look eastwards there was still the vast, barbaric untamed vision of Africa as it was in the beginning.

The dish that goes with this memory strangely enough is not pork or fish but goat. It is reprehensible how the goat is neglected in French and British Africa. When I praised the Portuguese for what they did for pork, I should have remembered goat as well, because they brought with them into Africa the respect the cooks of the Iberian peninsular always had for this Pan-like creature. In Angola they cooked it in several ways but the best version was one I had on a Sunday in the house of a small farmer. This house might have been in Madeira—square, clean, with a roof of red tiles. It had just three bedrooms and the kitchen served as a sitting-room because, in the winter and at night, it could be cold in these highlands. But it also had a parlour with a small square table in the centre that was used only for visitors. The table was covered with a home-made crochet cloth and set with chairs waxed and polished to look like the most expensive wood. It had, at the side, a stand with a vase of flowers and net curtains over the window panes. Some family portraits hung on the wall as well as a calendar marking religious feast days and a lithograph of Christ on the Cross. In these humble surroundings I was treated like a Roman emperor and fed and felt like one, particularly when, to my amazement, the meal was concluded with dishes full of fresh strawberries, not flown from Europe but grown in the soil of Angola, their savour positive and uplifting to fit the character of the blood-red earth of their birth.

Although Mozambique is further away in miles from Portugal than Angola, psychologically it was in some ways closer. This was due very largely to the fact that on the whole it received closer attention from the Metropolitan administration than Angola. The fact too that it possessed by far the finest harbours on the coast of East Africa made it a natural outlet for an interior which was being developed with great rapidity and purposefulness by the Dutch and British of Southern Africa. Through the capital, Lourenço Marques, already linked by rail to Johannesburg and Beira, the principal port for old Nyasaland and the Rhodesias, it was forced to keep pace with contemporary development in a way Angola never was. Moreover its lovely coastline and yellow beaches became a favourite holiday playground for the Europeans of the interior. All this gave

administration and hoteliers an unusually powerful incentive. At
the same time, as I have stressed before, its links with the East
remained close and solid, and thousands of citizens of the Portuguese
province of Goa on the coast of India, came to settle in Mozambique
adding a permanent Indian colour to the culture of the province.
Also there was no lack of manpower as in Angola. Less than two-
thirds the size of Angola, Mozambique contained almost half as
many more people. One of its most pofitable sources of revenue was
the export of surplus labour to the mines of South Africa.

Geographically it lacks the vast healthy highlands of Angola.
Most of it is comparatively low-lying country, for centuries haunted
with fever and sleeping-sickness. Its nature therefore is far more
intensely tropical, its agriculture and animal husbandry totally
different. Its rainfall is higher and it has well-watered lowlands
where crops like sugar and rice can be grown in abundance. It is
only in the north-west where there are plateaux and mountains on
the Angolan scale, above all in the purple, cloud-scraping peaks
of what we called the Livingstone Range on the eastern shores
of the great Lake Malawi. Moreover, Portuguese settlement in
Mozambique was not on the same scale as in Angola and not nearly
so many Portuguese were committed to the country. The pattern
of it all was still far more traditionally colonial than in Angola
though great changes were under way. All these factors made for a
totally different nuance in the cooking.

One factor then seemed a constant—the indigenous peoples,
mostly Bantu in origin, had no real contribution to make to the
art of Mozambique cooking. What I have said of their cooking in
Angola applied even more here. It is only through what they grow
and breed and the fish they net and trap that they influence the
eating habits of the land. From Lourenço Marques to Port Amelia
in the north, crustaceans took their place on the table almost as
naturally and familiarly as the sardine at home in Portugal. But all
that I have said about the expansion of towns, the development of
hotels and inns in connexion with Angola applied to Mozambique.

One result was that a traveller could be faced with the pale and
vapid products of international cuisine. With one or two exceptions,
one had to go to the more unpretentious restaurants, favoured by
the Portuguese living and working in the province, to get an idea
of Mozambique cooking, or better still, go to eat in the homes of
the Portuguese themselves.

The main dishes among the exceptions I have mentioned were the piri-piri dishes. Piri-piri was perhaps Mozambique's national dish and its main contribution to the art of cooking in Portuguese Africa. Piri-piri was, of course, not unknown in Angola. I do not know how, why or when it was evolved except that it must be a precious hang-over from the remote past. It has, for instance, achieved quite a standing in Nigeria. I have eaten amazing piri-piri dishes in Lagos or pilli-pilli, as it is called sometimes, on the Benin coast and I only refrained from mentioning it in my chapter on West Africa because it was native to Portuguese East Africa. It has achieved a certain popularity even in Lisbon but nowhere was piri-piri to consistently eaten as in Mozambique, particularly in Beira and the capital, where piri-piri feasts, if not piri-piri orgies, were organised for visitors from the interior. It is difficult to say which city or area was best at piri-piri but on the whole I think I would choose Lourenço Marques although I suspect my choice is influenced as much by the setting as by the excellence of the cooking. This clean, well-ordered city of ample design seemed to possess the flame-like plants and flowering trees to go with the taste of the dish.

After a day of swimming from one of the yellow beaches or sailing along a coast of feathered palm, the man who has become hooked on piri-piri hungers for his favourite dish like a junkie for heroin, because the person who has once acquired a taste in the tropics for Indian curries, Oriental spices or African chillies, becomes an addict. It is no good arguing that the spice and piri-piri principles in cooking are barbaric and ruinous to any sensitive palate as my French and Chinese friends do, boasting of how they have created the two ruling academies of the art of cooking in the world without such extremes. I can only say that in eating these sorts of dishes in the context of their own culture and climates and in making allowances above all for the choice of material confronting the cooks who use them, my admiration for them has increased over the years. Certainly my own love of the subtleties of French and Chinese food has not been impaired by my equal love of this way of cooking. Obviously I am not alone in my feelings for the restaurants and hotels, like the great Polana, always seemed full of piri-piri voluptuaries.

Of course every cook in Mozambique had his own particular way of preparing piri-piri. I have chosen one provided by a Portuguese housewife of Mozambique. According to her instructions, one begins by squeezing out some lemons, passing the juice through

a sieve, warming it in a pan, inserting peppers and chillies that must
be red (and freshly picked, she emphasised). They are simmered on
a low heat for just five minutes. The mixture is then taken from the
stove, separated from its juice and the peppers pressed into a fine
paste. A pinch of salt is added and the pounding continues until
there are no lumps left in the pulp. This pulp is returned to the pan
with the original lemon juice and further simmered while being
constantly stirred. This then is the piri-piri sauce which can be
eaten with steak, mutton, fowl, fish and crustacean and always best
I would say with rice of some kind to provide the exact civilising
corrective to the pagan incitement of the sauce.

This sort of food must be thought of in its own setting and there
was no setting quite like the island of Mozambique because it was,
in a sense, the other pole of the psychological axis around which
the Portuguese world of Africa revolved: a sort of historical Omega
to Madeira's Alpha. The island, since I first saw it from the deck
of a Japanese tramp steamer, had of course developed considerably,
but the fortress which Vasco da Gama started at the end of the
fifteenth century still dominated the shining foreshore and its fringe
of palm. There were still many of the old Portuguese houses left.
I have one in particular in mind, a house of faded pink and beautiful proportions, with an eurythmic gable to the roof. Down south
at the Cape of Good Hope we think of the gable which graces so
many an old Dutch and Huguenot house as our own invention.
But here it was in Mozambique to speak up for the inter-mingling
and interdependence of our histories and cultures in their African
beginnings which, consciously or unconsciously, fashioned our
respective characters. Thus, as I began with an island, I am compelled to end with an island, leaving this image of the gabled
building as a sort of custom house to pass through and so cross
over the frontier between the Portuguese world and my own native
world in the south.

That is how it all looked a few years ago. How does it look now?
I have no means of telling from personal experience. I can only
say that my fourth visit was abruptly ended at Luanda airport only
recently. I landed there at night, the airport swarming with black
teenage soldiers, cigarettes dangling from their lips, automatic rifles
swinging from their hips. Hardly had we landed when a battle
flared up round the airport and we were hustled back into our
aeroplane and sent off into the night without even the chance to

refuel. And as always when silent and alone high in the night over Africa, I was assailed by music from within. On this occasion it was like an echo speeding down some canyon of time—the memory of a fado, the traditional Portuguese ballad of fate I had heard everywhere in Angola and Mozambique when I was there last. It was the 'Una Casa Portuguese' sung so often and well by Amalia Rodrigues. More than ever it summed up many of the basic virtues of this misjudged and so unfairly misprised people. Yes, she would sing, in a Portuguese house there is always bread and wine on the table, and no matter who knocked on the door he was asked in to sit at the table. For in a Portuguese home, no matter how poor, the real wealth was in the capacity for giving. Four whitewashed walls, a smell of rosemary, some yellow grapes, geraniums and roses in the garden and a painting of the blessed St. Joseph on the wall, that and a promise of spring and love under the sun, was a Portuguese home for her.

I had known thousands of such homes in Angola and Mozambique and had never knocked on a single door and been turned away. I looked down below the rushing plane and not a light came back at me. What is the meaning of liberation and emancipation which demands that such homes and such people had to go?

CHAPTER SIX

Malays at the Cape

I DO not know what the Portuguese, who were, after all, the first Europeans to see it, called Table Mountain. Their whole imagination seems to have been taken up by the fact that they had rounded one of the southernmost capes of Africa and at last found a new way to the East. They called this cape first of all the Cape of Storms but changed it eleven years later to the Cape of Good Hope. Their greatest poet, indeed one of the greatest poets of the world, Camões, who sailed round the Cape to China not long after its discovery, saw it in a different light. In his *Lusiad* he invented a Titanic Negroid presence which emanated from the rocks and earth of the Cape, darkening the sky, to warn the hero of the poem that a time would come when Portugal would have to pay a terrible price for having broken into the new world beyond the Cape with such violence and greed. This invention of Camões is one of the most awesome vindications of the intuitive vision of the true artist because today his warning, uttered some four hundred years ago, could hardly be more apt. When one considers all the social, racial and moral turbulence of this age, one wonders whether the first name for the peninsula was not after all the right one and whether one should not revert to its original name, thinking of it as Camões did as that "far and much tormented Cape".

Yet, however, apt or inapt the final naming of the Cape, the Portuguese were undoubtedly right in regarding its rounding as the most fateful aspect of their voyage of discovery, because, in the process, not just a page but a whole book of ancient history was finally closed and a great new volume begun. But what has always been most mysterious to me is why the Portuguese, who anchored themselves in what were then so many unhealthy harbours and inlets on the west and east coasts of Africa, should never have settled at the Cape they themselves had discovered. Perhaps they shared, as a nation, some of Camõens's intuition and feared it instinctively from the beginning. Perhaps they were just mistrustful of the storms that blew up so suddenly and with such violence. Whatever the reason, though they called in at the Cape often for fresh water, they never made any effort to settle there even though the climate is the nearest southern Africa has to offer to that of their own part of Iberia. Other great sailors like Francis Drake could call it "the fairest Cape seen in the circumference of the whole of the earth", but the Portuguese remained curiously impervious to its attractions. When, nearly 120 years after Bartholomew Diaz had first rounded it, one of their greatest Viceroys, Francesco d'Alemeida and his bodyguard were murdered there by Hottentots, they stopped calling there even for water.

It was the Dutch who first saw its possibilities. Like the Portuguese, their sailors died from scurvy by the hundreds on the long voyages to the East. Already in 1602 the Dutch East Indiamen were anchoring regularly in Table Bay to refill their water barrels and scrounge around the countryside for green vegetables to act as anti-scorbutics. Gradually the idea came to them that, situated in a temperate zone and almost exactly half-way to their factories in the Far East, the Cape might be the ideal place for growing vegetables, fresh food and meat to revictual their ships and prevent the terrible loss of life at sea which sometimes caused their ships to return home with less than half their original crews. In 1652 the vital decision was taken to establish a settlement at the Cape but it was a settlement with a unique difference. Its one and only objective was to grow food and more food for the increasing number of Dutch ships trafficking between Europe and the Far East. It is the only incident in history I know of where a new country was occupied with a basic edict against colonisation and expansion.

The Dutch have always been a food-conscious people. They have always known how to cook and eat well if perhaps somewhat over robustly. The French gourmet and remarkable writer, Leon Daudet, son of the great Alphonse, in a book he wrote about the Low Countries just before the war, called their food the best in Europe, much to the annoyance of the French. In spite of a natural bias created by my ancestry, I would not go quite as far myself, although I would not attempt to denigrate all the good things that have come out of the great love of food of the Low Countries. This shows up remarkably clearly even in their painting. Indeed, one of the things I have against Dutch painting is that so much of it is a kind of apotheosis of good living, good food, good husbandry, physical well-being and all the material comforts that go with them. I long for it to be more troubled by self-doubt and anguish of spirit, but between Rembrandt and Van Gogh it hardly ever is. However, the food-consciousness of the founders of the settlement at the Cape of Good Hope was innocent enough because its motive was not self-indulgence but a matter of life and death. Once the battle against scurvy was won, this love of food of a Holland made *nouveau riche* by the trade in spice, quickly appeared as another incentive in life at the Cape and raised its standards of living and eating to far greater heights than in any other part of the New World.

It is no accident therefore that they called the mountain which dominates the Cape of Good Hope Table Mountain. It is true that to the eye of the sailor beating up over the horizon the long summit looks as flat as a table top. It is true too that when the wind blows from the south-east, driving moisture from the warm Indian Ocean to meet the cold air over the Atlantic, a white cloud is formed. For days this cloud will lie flat and even on the mountain and wrap itself round the precipitous slopes like a sheet of white linen and to the wishful thinking of the Dutch sailors the temptation was irresistible. They immediately called it the table cloth of Table Mountain. Even the wide bay at the foot of the mountain was called Table Bay.

I could think of other metaphors, perhaps more poetic and evocative, but I must confess that all these similies gathered around the central image of a table, symbolise, as perhaps no others could have done, all that was involved at the beginning of the first European settlement at the Cape. The necessities and the obsessions were all about food and it is not surprising perhaps that, with such beginnings. it is here in the south that the richest, the most original, most complex and civilised contribution to the art of cooking in Africa evolved. I would go even further and say that, if it had not been for the opening of the Suez Canal and the quicker modern, methods of transportation and communication which went with it, making it impossible for the way of life which started at the Cape of Good Hope and gradually spread north into the interior of Africa to continue in the role it possessed in the beginning, the way of cooking evolved there might have become one of the greatest in the world. I say this not to lessen the present achievement of cooking in southern Africa but, in a way, to emphasise the vast potential for making, as it were, a new synthesis of all the systems of cooking in the world which was dynamic in this first small settlement at the foot of Table Mountain.

There was first of all the physical situation. The Cape lay well within the temperate zone of the southern hemisphere. To one like myself who was born and bred in the remote interior of Africa, it looks in fact not at all like a part of Africa but a part of the Mediterranean. Deep down I cannot feel the emotions about it that I have about other parts of my native land. It had the earth, the climate and the rainfall to grow and produce anything that could be grown in Europe. Besides, it was half-way between Europe and the East, with access to all the cultures of Arabia, Persia, India, and the countries beyond and with access, above all, to their arts of cooking, which were more advanced than in Europe.

That we started life as a half-way house to the East was the outstanding aspect of our history continually drummed into us at school. This fact in every sense dominates our beginning and explains why our subsequent development was all provisional—the pun may be apt but is unintentional. The settlement at the Cape was only a half-way step towards the fulfilment of the purpose which brought it into being. For people like myself, deeply opposed to our divisive present, our life in South Africa remains not whole but profoundly provisional.

Originally, in this happy physical situation, in its position at a cross-roads of history, in its role as a gigantic kind of inn on the long and dangerous way between East and West, the Cape was the natural meeting-place of both. The Dutch brought back with them from their growing empire in the Far East not only new knowledge and techniques but Javanese, Indian and above all Malay slaves to work in the gardens they had established, after the most difficult of beginnings, at the Cape. This traffic in slaves grew rapidly because of the development of farms and vineyards which, against all the intentions and endeavours of the founders, the settlers were creating for themselves. These resolute and rebellious men, the Free Burghers as they called themselves, very soon had all the land that could be cultivated around Table Mountain and the Peninsula firmly in their grip.

That done, they began to reach out, despite official discouragement from Europe, into the broad and fertile valleys of the purple

Hottentots-Holland mountains which dominated the horizon to the north. Hard on this came almost an explosion of population to compel further expansion: for suddenly large numbers of French refugees arrived. They were the famous Huguenots who, after the Revocation of the Edict of Nantes, fled from France. Many of them came from the Bordeaux area, around Protestant strongholds like La Rochelle, to bring not only French cooking but also a stock of their native vines to start the great vineyards of the Cape. Later, they were joined by Germans and other Europeans who added their own concepts of agriculture and cooking.

Last of all, some 150 years after the beginning, came the British. For all their vast contribution, technological and administrative, and for all the tolerance, freedom of thought and rule of law they gave to the country, I personally believe they did nothing but harm in the kitchen. Fortunately, by that time the Cape way of cooking was deeply enough rooted to stand a great deal of shock and possessed resilience enough to recover from outside damage.

Of other European influences apart from Dutch, the French one was most important because it provided a corrective of refinement to the basic Low Country concept of food. Moreover it was not left solely to the Cape French to promote Gallic influence. There was a constant coming and going of French ships and at one time the influence of France on the settlement was so great, the light-hearted and elegant touch they introduced so pronounced, that they offended the sober Dutch administration. One soured Dutch governor solemnly tried to limit French fashions at the Cape, going so far as to determine the height of heel and length of dress the women at the Cape wore.

It is most remarkable how soon after its foundation the art of cooking was so far advanced in the Cape that what Heine wrote in one of his essays about Holland, could almost have been written about the Cape at the beginning of the eighteenth century.

"As far as Dutch cooking is concerned," Heine proclaimed, "it is distinguished by its cleanliness and secondly by its toothfullness. The way they dress fish is particularly delightful. The touchingly devout and yet profoundly sensuous fragrance of celery, the self-conscious naivete of garlic. It is, however, reprehensible that they wear flannel under-garments—not the fishes but the beautiful daughters of the sea-girt Holland." It is a fact of our history that the earliest of the daughters of Holland who accompanied their husbands to the Cape on the business of the Honourable East India Company not only brought their flannel underwear with them but also their gift of cooking. There may have been some underground psychological connexion between the two. Anyway, it was this staunch gift of the Dutch for cooking that was the aboriginal stock on which the great flowering of the art of cooking that followed was first grafted. The gift certainly needed to be tough if it were not to be utterly overwhelmed by the new possibilities, the wealth of materials and spices that assailed established ways with increasing pressure from every ship homeward bound from the East. Besides, the slaves, who not only worked in the gardens, vineyards and farms, but soon became cooks, maintained their own tastes and traditions. It was not long before they had a substantial say of their own in matters of taste and cooking. Above all they had an invaluable experience of cooking in tropical climates and so of the art of preserving food against decay. This, of course, was of enormous importance to sailors who had to spend months in the tropics and hitherto hardly knew any other method of preserving meat beyond keeping it in brine. The increasing Oriental population of the Cape soon taught them many other and more delightful ways. The Cape quickly acquired such a world-wide reputation on this score alone that the pirate and hydrographer William Dampier wrote with the utmost appreciation of the fish pickled at the Cape for sailors and noted the fact that it was also exported "in great quantities yearly to Europe". It is this meeting at the Cape of the experience, culture, knowledge and sometimes wisdom of East and West which led to a kind of unbridled gastronomic miscegination and produced a numerous progeny of spiced and coloured dishes that gave cooking in South Africa the unique character and stature it possesses today.

Since the slaves were the first cooks, working under the be-flanneled matrons of every household, historical justice demands that their contribution to South African cooking should have priority. The core of this section of the settlement was what we call Malay. Although many of them were Malayan, the term applies to numbers of others, originally inhabitants of Malacca, the northern parts of Sumatra, Java and the bright twist of islands the Dutch East India Company brought under its rule as far to the east as Ambom. They were called Malay because they all spoke Malay, which was the esperanto of that world, and because almost all of them, by the time the Dutch encountered them, had become Muslims of some denomination. A common language and a common faith held them together. In time, another and greater world of coloured people grew up around them who picked up many of their customs, above all their taste in food: they are the people called "Cape coloured" today. These were of so mixed an origin that it is impossible to sort out the different strands of brightly coloured human material that went into the weaving of their character. Only one thing is certain; they were begotten by European fathers who either married women of colour in the beginning or who had illicit relationships with them. We know little more than that these women were drawn not only from the population I have called Malay but also from Hottentots, Bushmen and, even later, from the Bantu from the interior. As slaves and workers they were forced into the same sort of occupations as the Malays and lived in close contact with them without ever really becoming an integral part of the Malay community. Yet, paradoxically, they tended to identify with the Europeans rather than either Malays, or the Indians and Singhalese who came later, let alone the Bantu. The majority adopted Cape Dutch as their language, became Christians and accompanied the Dutch and Huguenot French of the Cape on their thrust into the interior while the Malays themselves, on the whole, clung to their religion and their original occupations in the Cape, particularly the area around the mountain.

To this day the Malays have retained, despite all modern pressures, some identity of their own and still speak a strange form of Malay. But the Cape-coloured population, so closely linked to them by fate and circumstance, maintain the language of their fathers and tend to follow the customs of the so-called European in South Africa. Socially they lead a tragic twilight sort of existence as an increasingly large yet isolated community, quintessentially inclined towards the European but rejected by them and psychologically incapable of merging with the other coloured peoples of the land. Yet for all that they have a vitality, a gaiety, a love of living which makes their European overlords look insipid and joyless. I shall have more to say about them later but it is important at the beginning to realise that the contribution to the art of cooking which we are considering came not from them but from the Malays.

I never realised how great that contribution was until I had been to Malaya, Sumatra, Java, Lombok, Celebes, Timor, Ambom and all the other islands which were once the possessions of the East India Company. I remember coming back to Cape Town after the war in 1948, straight from Java. I was still in uniform. I stood in the main street, amazed at fate, because for some eight years I had never seriously thought that I could survive to set eyes on it all again. The street led straight from what is left of the kitchen gardens of John Company to the statue of Jan Van Riebeeck, the man who first planted them. He stood there in bronze, looking out north across the placid waters of Table Bay towards the blue mountains of the interior he had been forbidden to enter. It was not an unattractive statue, oddly elegant and delightfully incongruous because his pose, cane, ruffles and all was not unlike that of a French fop of his own day. Suddenly I became aware that the coloured people around about me were talking neither English nor Afrikaans but a kind of Malay. I went up to one of the flower sellers. The Cape peninsula has more varieties of flowers, I believe, than any other area of the world of a comparable size and out of a compulsion to celebrate my return and, I suppose, sheer gratitude for still being alive, I bought more flowers than I wanted and paid the flower seller far more than I should have. Taken by surprise, she instinctively thanked me and, not suspecting that I knew the language, she turned to a neighbourhing flower seller and, in that lightning-quick manner of all Cape-coloureds, exclaimed in Malay: "This Orang Blanda must be mad to be so nice." "Orang Blanda" is the name used to this day for the people of Holland wherever Malay is spoken. Small as the incident was, it was a significant demonstration to me of how the Malays still remembered their original identity. Having learned Malay in the war my mind went on logically from there to measure the extent to which the language which is spoken by the descendants of the European settlement in the Cape, Afrikaans, had been shaped at base by the language of Malaya, for this has much to do with cooking too. I had of course always been aware that numbers of words in Afrikaans were originally Malay but until then I had not known that the grammar, the actual mechanism of Afrikaans, was largely of a Malayan pattern. For instance, unlike the Dutch of Holland, the grammar of Afrikaans has no gender and no number. This, of course, is one of the outstanding characteristics of Malay. It explains why it is one of the easiest languages in the world to learn and why it is the official language of so large a part of South-East Asia today. The vocabulary

of Afrikaans may be almost entirely of Dutch origin with traces
here and there in speech and inflection of French influence—a
double negative, for example—but its basic organisation is largely
Malay. It is a sad reflection on our present state of mind in South
Africa that this fact is not openly acknowledged. By now there are
enough philologists who study Malay and who know the truth. It is
all part of the increasingly sharp race and colour prejudice of the
new rulers of the land who make men afraid to admit the contribution that the peoples of colour they reject socially and politically
have made to something so intimate as the language they speak, let
alone enter into the mixed composition of the blood that runs in
their own veins. All this is a great pity because Afrikaans is a wonderful language, worthy of honest appreciation since it is made to
measure for expressing the new and mixed reality of the modern
South Africa. Yet it is not for this reason that I raise the matter.
It may be the most remarkable and conclusive illustration of how
profound and intimate is the contribution of the Malays to the South
African way of life, but I mention it because it goes to the heart of
our concept of cooking. This language the Malays helped to evolve
even in my own youth, when the Dutch of Holland was still one of
the two official languages of the country—English was the other—
was referred to as "Kombuis Taal"—kitchen language. Today, as
Afrikaans, it has taken the place of the original Dutch, but it is still
"kitchen language" in the best sense of the term. So let us follow it
as "kitchen language" to the beginnings.

Now one of the most depressing factors of eating in southern
Africa, as I remember it from my childhood, is the complete
absence of our national dishes from the menus of hotels, restaurants
and the dining-cars of trains in which we often had to live from
three to five days on end. This rule was imposed by the British, who
controlled the railways, ran the hotels and patronised the restaurants.
Afrikaans South Africans, like my own family, hardly ever stayed
in hotels.

We tended to think of hotels and, for that matter, restaurants as
places invented for friendless people like the official British, com-
mercial travellers and speculators in horses and cattle. In fact, if a
member of an Afrikaans community was reduced to staying at an
hotel in the interior, one automatically thought that he must be a
shady character and had been deprived for some disreputable reason
of the contacts his family naturally had with Afrikaans people all

over the country from the Cape to the Zambezi river. We were a close community, small in number and, however thinly and widely spread over the southern part of the continent, everybody had some connexion or other with everybody else. Normally when we travelled, no matter where we went, we had a family to call on and a home in which we would automatically be asked to stay. If we had to go on vacation to the sea as we sometimes did for a month or two, the normal practice was to take a house and to invade it with one's own servants and live there as one lived at home.

The one happy exception I can still remember was Cape Town. There were, it is true, no hotels which served our national food. But there were excellent boarding-houses which specialised in our native dishes. Many had a distinguished clientele, members of Parliament from the Afrikaans interior like my father, for instance, who preferred the food there to the excellent international menus of hotels like the old Queen's, the vanished Royal Hotel and Arthur's Seat at Sea Point or the Mount Nelson. Above all there were first-class restaurants serving traditional South African food like the famous White House in Strand Street.

The great South African poet Leipoldt, who loved his food and wrote two eloquent books about cooking in a prose which not only makes them valuable guides to cooking but works of literature, and who was a close friend of mine although I was much younger than he, has some exciting descriptions of how well one ate at the White House. Eating there was one of the most precious of his memories and I well remember how, talking to me about it one day he added: "Of course the cooks were all Malay Ayahs."

At the beginning of the century, Cape Town contained not just restaurants owned by Europeans with Malays doing the cooking, but actually knew a period when it was full of eating houses or cook-shops kept by Malays themselves. These had a tremendous reputation for cleanliness and good food. They specialised in Oriental dishes and the people of the Cape, before they became corrupted by the racial prejudices and the fanatical puritanism of my countrymen from the interior, patronised the Malay eating houses openly and freely because the food, apart from the fact that it was clean and tasty, was cheap. Alas, all this has changed and this kind of boarding house and restaurant has vanished for ever. So one has to go into the homes of the Cape Malays, still as clean and full of self-respect as their eating-houses were, to sample the sort of food they brought

with them nearly three hundred years ago. Considering the small-
ness of their number, the pressures of all kinds exerted consciously
or unconsciously against the retention of their separate identity, it
is miraculous to me that they still cook and eat as they do. Much of
this of course has to do with their religion, for however modern
their appearance and their role in the economy of South Africa,
they still observe the great Muslim feasts like Ramadan and its
Bachannalian opposite, Lebaran.

They themselves compare Lebaran to our Christmas. Should one
enter a Malay household in the course of the day which precedes
the feasting, one would find every female in the household, from the
smallest girl to the grandmother, busy preparing the scores of
different dishes to be consumed that night. Despite the sheer physical
exhaustion produced by the long fasting of Ramadan, the bustle is
frantic. I have always been amazed at this sudden uprush of energy,
the noise, the movement, the sounds of pestles ringing out in iron
mortars as they stamp out the cinnamon bark, dried chillies and a
dozen or more other herbs and spices for the evening meal; the
heightened voices rising to an almost hysterical pitch as they issue
orders and instructions to one another; and above all at the scent
of cooking, both pungent and subtle and evoking all the scents of
Arabia. On this day such foods which we claim as purely Afrikaans,
like sosatie, bobotie, bredie, koeksisters, kerries, pickled fish, yellow
rice, and the accompanying blatchangs, atjars and sambals, all
eaten with mountains of snow white rice, are being prepared in
such quantities that family kitchens are often too small and some of
the cooking has to be done on primus stoves and improvised fires in
the narrow back yards. Even such an esoteric feast as the Lebaran-
Hadji is still observed. A goat without blemish, dressed in coloured
silks, its horns decorated with white linen, is sacrificed and most of
the meat given to the poor. The women still gather in one another's
houses in the afternoon wearing jewels and silks which have come
down in the family and which cast a sunset glow in the shadows, to
drink cups of milky tea, laced with their favourite spice, and eat
brightly coloured cakes à la Javanese, arranged on trays covered
with silver or gold tinsel, and the many varieties of delicious home-
made Malay preserves which they, stimulated and inspired by the
example of the Huguenots, have raised to one of the highest
culinary arts.

This is one of the rare occasions when the Malay women play

and their men work in the kitchen because it is their duty for once
to prepare the prescribed buryani. It is usually made in three stages.
The rice is cooked first with only a little salted water, a wooden fork
being used to stir the rice often enough to prevent it from burning.
Just before the rice is done, some butter is added. Then comes a
leg of mutton (fish is sometimes used in exactly the same way, it
tastes different but just as good), boned and diced, well washed,
put in a pot with some sliced onion, some pounded green ginger,
fennel, garlic and cumin seeds as well as some sliced tomatoes. All
this is left to simmer quietly until the meat is nearly cooked. Last of
all the rice is taken out of the pot in which it has been cooked with
only a small layer left behind in the bottom. The meat is placed
on this layer and the pot is then filled with alternative layers of the
meat and rice with, very often some sliced hard boiled eggs placed
in between. The last layer of all must be rice over which some
saffron, previously dissolved in a little boiling stock, is poured. The
lid of the saucepan is then pressed down tightly and if necessary
some laundry irons put on top to keep it in position. The more
slowly this dish is cooked the nicer it is and the men do it with a
tenderness and delicacy wholly unexpected when one remembers
how hard and exacting if not brutal are the occupations they are
compelled to follow. They prefer a slow, charcoal fire and let the
meat simmer, sealed in its cast iron pot, for many hours. Nothing
will ever persuade them to unseal their dish before they reckon it
is finished. How they know when the right moment has come, is
not conditioned entirely by experience; I, who watched them do it
often as a child, am still certain it is done by a mixture of the
intuition of the inspired cook that most men deep down are, and
a perception of a change in the nature of a faint kind of incense which
despite all the sealing, comes to one's nose from the simmering pot.

I have chosen to examine this dish in particular detail because it
represents one of the purest Malay dishes still to be found at the
Cape. In fact I have eaten almost its exact equivalent in Java
except that the Javanese ended with a cup of coffee instead of
"flou tea"—flou, is an Afrikaans word which literallly means faint
but is obviously meant to imply weak.

The Malay equivalent of baptism, the naming of the child, birth-
days and anniversaries, the day a boy completes his catechism of
the Koran—Tamat—funeral feasts and of course weddings, are celebrated with feats of traditional food, while Sunday, without religious

significance for them, is a natural day for eating much and well. But it is true that, just as the Dutch originally learned from the Malays, the Malays learned from the Dutch to the extent that they describe their complete system of cooking today as the authentic cooking of the Cape Dutch. But on feast days, what is purely Malay in their cooking tends to assert itself, and I shall disentangle Dutch and Malay as much as possible and concentrate entirely on this. The Dutch contribution can speak for itself later in the language of its own kitchen.

One general observation to convey the atmosphere in which all this kind of cooking and eating is done; I spent five and a half years of my life in Java, my own sense of perception heightened by the exactions of war. In that time I got to know the Javanese well and I read my Stanford Raffles from beginning to end, again and again. He loved the Javanese and was loved in return by them as no other ruler had ever been before in Indonesian history and when I last ate with Malay friends a remark that Raffles made about the Javanese seemed to me as applicable to the Malays of the Cape:

"It is not sufficient," Raffles said, "that the man should place good food before his guest; he is bound to do more. He should render the meal palatable by kind words and treatment; to soothe him after his journey and to make his heart glad while he partakes of refreshment."

I suspect, however, that it was not merely through dishes sanctified and preserved by religious custom that the Malays, in the first instance, influenced cooking in South Africa. It was their knowledge of preserving food in hot climates which provided the thin end of the wedge for influencing the stout and obdurate Dutch in the art of cooking. I say this all the more confidently because it was their skill in preserving and pickling vegetables and fish for the scurvy-stricken sailors of John Company that first made Cape cooking celebrated in the Antarctic world.

The Malays were also expert fishermen and sailors, immediately at home in the seas of the Cape which were as rich as any in the world with astonishing varieties of fish. The peninsula happens to be a kind of geological breakwater that divides the Indian from the Atlantic Ocean. On the west of the peninsula flows the broad, deep, icy Antarctic current, a sort of Gulf Stream in reverse, penetrating as far north as the coast of Angola, and bringing with it all the fish and mammals that live in it from porpoises to whales and the birds that prey on the fish, from penguins to albatrosses. On the east, barely fifteen miles away, the Indian Ocean washes warm against the yellow sands and purple cliffs, full of another rich fish life of its own. There was not, and never has been, any lack of material for such gifted fishermen as the Malays, just as there was no lack of incentive to send them fishing. The local demand for fresh fish was easily met, and the bulk of the catch was preserved.

They set about preserving in two different ways: one was by splitting the fish open, removing the entrails and leaving them, salted, to dry. This not only furnished the needs of the East Indiamen but produced in time one of the great national dishes of the land: smoor-vis. What could accompany sailors on their long voyages across the oceans could obviously accompany the settlers on their thrust into the interior. The other was the far more famous "Ingelegde vis" which attracted Dampier's attention and quickly became a popular export to Europe.

Every Malay household in South Africa, for that matter every Afrikaans household, has its own ideas on how "Ingelegde" fish is best done. Some will fry the fish first in batter, some in breadcrumbs, but to good Malay cooks this is an unnecessary and barbaric heresy, with a chance that the product might not last as well. The best way is still the original way. The fish is sliced and the slices well washed so that no blood or other internal matter is left clinging to it. They are then dried and fried in oil. Meanwhile onions—the quantity depends largely on personal taste—are finely sliced, placed in a dish with just enough red vinegar to cover them. Some salt and pepper, chillies, turmeric, curry powder, green ginger, a little brown sugar and a few bay leaves are added and left to stand for some hours. This mixture is then brought to the boil as slowly as possible and the scum which rises in the process is removed with a wooden spoon—metal, our old African cooks were adamant, spoilt the taste. This mixture should boil up once only because it is most important that the onions remain as fresh and crisp as possible. Meanwhile the golden-brown fried fish is drained and placed in a preserving jar and the sauce is poured over it.

This way of preserving fish was so popular that it was the one exception to the ban on South African food in hotels. Until some years ago, for instance, it was still obtainable daily at lunch in the Mount Nelson Hotel in Cape Town, and I could still get it regularly at my club. The taste for international cooking, however, has so grown that it has vanished even from these privileged tables and is now to be found only in the homes of the Malays and Cape-coloured people who cherish it as one of the best things that have come down from the past.

I well remember how in my own childhood days, before refrigeration existed, my mother, on our vacations by the sea, would take two cooks with her, two wonderful, fat, lovable and expert black African ladies, who knew beter even than my mother what pleased our child-like palates. From the moment we arrived at the Cape until we left six weeks or two months later to return to the remote interior, one of the ladies—they took turns at it—was always hard at work pickling fish to take back home with us. Between them they pickled it on such a scale that we would not have enough screw-top bottles, which were very expensive in those days. We were reduced to using the tins emptied of the popular golden syrup produced by a firm called Lyles under the heraldic legend: "*Honi soit qui mal y pense*", which we, as children, with some mispronounciation, turned into a wistful pun proclaiming the truth, so important to us, that "Hunger made empty stomachs". These green and gold tins were washed out thoroughly, filled with pickled fish and the original lids were firmly clamped into position. When we had twelve score or more of these tins full and assembled we would call in a local carpenter to solder down the lids and make sure they were air-tight. I remember too that it was always the custom among Afrikaans people in those days to bring gifts with them for their friends wherever they went. On our journeys to the coast we would bring them our ideas of luxuries like canned fruit and biltong—of which more later—when they came to visit us, high in the priority of their gifts came "Inglelede vis".

The other form of preserving fish taught to us by the Malays was drying and curing. It played an important role in opening up the African interior and was part of our lives until refrigeration became widely available. The Malays were great experts. To this day the great Malay fishing communities of South-East Asia have an expertise in preserving fish that makes our smoked herrings and their sour Scandinavian equivalents look like poor relations. The greatest fishing city in the world is Malayan, a vast town on stilts on the coast of Sumatra. I have visited it and seen the ingenuity of the Malays in drying, smoking and curing anything from the smallest shrimps to the biggest shark. Merchants come from places as far apart as Manila and Canton to buy their produce. This great art was transported to the Cape and applied specially to a kind of sea pike we call snoek. Unfortunately this fish is in grave disrepute in Europe. Immediately after the war it was a music hall joke in London. It was all started by a brother of mine who, as South African Trade Commissioner in London during the war, persuaded the South African Government to export snoek out of a desire to help the severely rationed people of Great Britain. The conservative British reacted in exactly the same manner as the famous Lady Anne Barnard to whom we owe such an incomparable description of life at the Cape at the end of the eighteenth century. "Salted and dried," she said, "snoek is one of the best fish at the Cape. This made a most incomparable mess [I suppose mess in the sense of a potage] though one I never desire to partake of again from its unaccountable singularity." If only the British public had had our South African recipes for dealing with snoek they might have reacted differently and understood why the Malays and Cape-coloured people watch their nets being hauled in, heavy with its catch of this sparkling blue, quick-silver fish, and exclaim, almost as if uttering some kind of Halleluyah: "This is our food."

This snoek was their favourite fish for salting, smoking and curing in the sun. When I was a boy on holiday at the Cape, the white walls of the fishermen's cottages everywhere along the coast seemed festooned with lines on which the spliced snoek was drying and dancing like laundry in the off-sea breeze. Dried snoek is by far the finest of all materials for making one of our greatest national dishes: "smoor-vis". It is to us what morue was to the Midi of France. The word smoor means both 'smothering' and 'braising', and the two meanings combined give a complete idea of the way in which the cured snoek is prepared by the Malays.

First, they smother the dried fish in water, overnight if necessary, to remove the salt. They then skin and bone it and press out the water, meticulously as if they are life-savers preserving it from drowning. They braise some onions in oil until they are a deep brown. If the onions are small they braise them whole, if not they do them rather coarsely diced. To these, they will add some red chillies according to taste and some raw potatoes cut into small cubes. When these are cooked, the fish, which has meanwhile been flaked, is added, the whole stirred together with a wooden fork or spoon and braised until the mixture is nice and brown all over. No salt or pepper is added in the preparation. In the interior, we always added some pimentos, skinned and sliced. We also added tomatoes, obviously a European fancy. Indeed every European household in the interior had their own variations to add to the basic Malay requirements. But whether in its original form or its more sophisticated European development, this became a national dish of great strategic importance in the battle for a balanced diet in the interior of Africa. People like myself who grew up there have such profound associations with it from our earliest childhood on that the mere sound of its name starts my mouth watering like a Pavlovian dog at the ringing of a dinner bell.

These two Malay contributions have figured at the head of the list because of their important role in the battle for survival of the sailors and pioneers who made the Cape. Yet even when the battle was won and the people of the expanding settlement could relax and think of food more in terms of what was tasty than just of what was sheer necessity, the Malays gave us other dishes that are so much part of our national way of life, they have become almost mystical, sacramental substances rather than food for vulgar consumption.

I speak first of bobotie, sosaties and bredie which have become national dishes *par excellence*. If one has to be put before the other, bobotie must come first. It is to South Africa what moussaka is to Greece. Sosaties are what shish-kebab is to Afghanistanis; bredie what goulash is to Hungarians. To hear South African cooks arguing about the best way of preparing bobotie, sosaties and bredie is like listening in to a metaphysical argument of such acute refinement that they might be medievalists disputing how many angels could balance on the point of a needle. The air of unreality is reinforced by the fact that so few of us have any awareness of the debt we owe the Malays in bringing us these three great gifts of the national kitchen.

First of all, bobotie. The poet Leipoldt, who I have already mentioned, told me once that he found a description of a dish very like bobotie in a cookery book printed in Europe as long ago as 1609—that is forty-three years before the creation of John Company's kitchen gardens at the Cape of Good Hope but still five years after the Dutch had finally established their first factory in Java. I believe one of the reasons bobotie caught on so quickly at the Cape was because, like moussaka, the meat used in making it is minced before cooking. I say this with some confidence because before the Dutch could introduce their own breeds of cattle and sheep to the Cape, the only meat obtainable was either game, of which, strangely enough, there is little mention in early records, or more commonly the cattle and fat-tailed sheep they could barter from the Hottentots. This meat was inevitably tough and edible only either highly marinaded, which did not become a serious possibility until the wine industry was established years later, stewed, as the Malays did in bredies, or minced as in bobotie. The basic minimum for bobotie was minced meat, a little soaked bread (in my own family cookery book, cold soft-cooked rice or mashed sweet potato is given in place of bread and, since bread clearly is not a Malay invention, I believe these ingredients to be nearer to the original Malay custom), eggs, some ghee or butter, finely chopped onion, garlic, some of the Malay's favourite mixture of curry powders and turmeric. These are all mixed together, put in a pie dish with a good deal of dripping and then baked in the oven for a while. The moment the mixture starts browning, the dish is extracted from the oven and some eggs, beaten up with milk, are poured over the meat. The Malays prefer to stick some lemon leaves into the mixture beforehand or, if they cannot get these, use bay leaves instead, but I have been told that orange or lemon leaves give the bobotie a more delicate flavour. The dish is then put back in the oven and baked very slowly until it is a healthy brown. The pace of the cooking is important because if the oven is too hot the bobotie will be too dry and that must never happen, because it is meant to be eaten moist, with rice as the main accompaniment.

This, roughly, I believe, was bobotie in the beginning but it is no longer the bobotie eaten in South Africa except in Malay homes. The dish has become more and more elaborate and more pretentious and I have become quite used to encountering it on my travels round the world in almost unrecognisable forms. This is a great pity because it is a first-rate dish. Moreover there are legitimate refinements that undoubtedly add to the quality of the original and give it its authentic modern idiom in taste. In my own home, for instance, we add a handful of finely chopped blanched almonds and some raisins to the mixture. Also, we avoid adding the egg and milk mixture half way through baking—a process which can so easily turn bobotie into a stodgy kind of baked custard. We beat bread-crumbs fried in dripping into the mixture. This somehow breaks up the rubbery texture of the baked eggs and milk. We add this covering mixture late and cook it quickly in a hotter oven. We also use the juice of a lemon to counteract the quite substantial amount of dripping instead of the wine vinegar favoured in the Cape. The great and unique Hildagonda Duckitt, the Mrs. Beeton of South Africa, in a first edition of her famous book on cooking *Where is it?* which I possess, says that a dessert spoon of brown sugar should be added as well, and that an ounce of tamarind soaked in boiling water and then strained and used instead of vinegar gives the dish an exceptionally pleasant, tart flavour. The tamarind juice I am sure was the original Malay ingredient. I must emphasise, however, that these are only some of the many variations of bobotie. There are as many boboties as there are homes in South Africa.

The name sosaties is derived from the Malay *sate* which means 'a spiced sauce' and *sesate* meaning 'meat on a skewer'. They are usually made of mutton cut into small square bits, suitable for spiking on thin bamboo skewers. The Malays originally marinaded the squares of meat, after a thorough washing and drying, in a mixture made of thinly shredded onions, fried preferably in fat rendered from the lamb's tail, their favourite curry powder, chillies, garlic and a generous quantity of tamarind juice. They usually did this in the early afternoon and left the meat in the mixture until it was wanted for cooking the next day. They would then skewer the meat with alternate pieces of mutton fat and roast them on an open fire, or, in the cities where fires were not available, fry them in a heavy frying-pan. Just before the sosaties were ready they would braise the marinaded mixture in another saucepan until the ingredients were cooked and reduced and then serve the sosaties with rice and this braised mixture as a sauce. Nowadays it is quite common to do sosaties with the squares of mutton and layers of bacon rather than fat. Served just with plain, well-cooked rice, it is, I think, preferable to bobotie. It is truly one of the great dishes of South Africa and what is particularly attractive about it is that, while bobotie has to be made at home, one can cook sosaties on safari or picnic, since they can be preserved in their own marinade for quite a while. Roasted over charcoal, flavoured with the smoke of the authentic wild wood of Southern Africa made more fragrant by natural herbs thrown from time to time on the fire, it is one of the finest out-door dishes that one can possibly imagine.

Even the smell of sosaties grilling at night in the bush of Africa today never fails to join the child in me, who first ate it on the banks of the Orange River in the Free State, to the man who met its equivalent so often during the war in villages lost in the jungles of the Sunda lands of Java and afterwards in the streets and market places of Singapore, Malacca, Kuala Lumpur and the ancient city of Batavia, now called Djakarta. There, street hawkers still carry bamboo yokes across their shoulders from which are suspended a charcoal brazier at one end and, at the other, a whole series of little dishes piled on top of one another in a light wicker container. At the drop of a cent they will sit down, extract sosaties already skewered, spiced and marinaded and grill them there and then for instant consumption with a steaming bowl of rice.

Last of the three, however great its popularity, I put the South African bredies. Leipoldt, for once surprisingly disparaging says: "Bredies are *nothing but* the meat and vegetable mixtures that were the fashion in the middle ages for the south of France, Spain and Italy"—the italics are mine. He should have known better because he knew his Far East, having visited it as a young ship's doctor. Of course, every country in the world has its meat stews—the Irish theirs, the English Lancashire hotpot, the Dutch hutspot, the German fientopf and the Hungarians their goulash which comes nearest to the great tomato bredies made in South Africa. But that the form in which we know the dishes in South Africa is Malay in origin is beyond doubt. The word 'bredie' certainly suggests how Asian it is. According to the great eighteenth-century traveller Lichtenstein, the word is Malagash and there has been a constant coming and going between the east coast of Madagascar and the world of India and Malaya ever since recorded history began. Cape cookery books have no hesitation in calling it a Cape Malay dish as the meticulous Hildagonda does.

All Malay bredies begin by braising finely sliced onions until they are brown in mutton fat, ghee, butter or oil in that order of precedence. Meat or fish is then added, laid on the onions and gently braised. The chosen vegetables, sliced and cut, are then placed on top of the meat with various seasonings but with red chillies always a *must*. I believe that one of the earliest forms of bredie at the Cape was the pumpkin variety because the Dutch, who introduced pumpkins into the country, at first despised it and regarded it as food fit only for their slaves. Today it has become almost sacramental. Provided the pumpkin is not mushy but firm and crisp, it is an excellent way of preparing the dish. Some Malays add only a little salt, a few chillies and a potato or two to the pumpkin. Others flavour it with green ginger, some sticks of cinnamon laid at the bottom of the dish and a few cloves and a little chopped garlic, and avoid potatoes, preferring to eat it with rice, cooked separately. The varieties are endless. I have had wonderful cauliflower bredies, others made of green peas, of curried beans, of Swedish turnips, kohlrabi, perslane, celery, carrots, peas, button turnips as well as spinach bredie, quickened by the additional of sorrel, which might be the original form because, according to Lichtenstein, bredie in Malagash means spinach. However, the form which stimulates both palate and patriotic fervour is undoubtedly tomato bredie—South Africa's own goulash.

I have some dozen recipes for doing tomato bredie all of which are good but I think the one given in Hilda's *Where is it?* is as good as any. All bredies start in the way I have already described except that here the mutton, after being filleted, must be cut up into small pieces and browned with onions. At home we used to separate fat from meat and braise the fat separately to prevent the dish from becoming greasy. Some dozen or more large tomatoes are either cut into slices or passed through a mincing machine. If the tomatoes are not quite ripe, some sugar and salt as well as the traditional red chillies are added. The braised meat, crisp fat and tomato are then stewed as slowly as possible. It is essential that the final result should not be watery. If necessary the lid is removed from the pot towards the end, the heat increased and the contents reduced to a rich, thick gravy. Up-country, where the mutton tended to be fatter than average, we used to add some peeled, cored and sliced ripe quinces to the mixture, toning down the sharpness of the quince with a slight addition of sugar. To my mind there is no stew, goulash or hotpot, call it what you like, to equal bredie done this way and eaten with some simple but perfect rice.

No consideration of the Malay contribution to the national dishes of South Africa can be complete without mentioning the chutneys, atjars and sambals they brought with them into their exile. But it is important to remember that between the few dishes I have already mentioned and atjars and sambals, there is a whole world of cooking not touched upon. Those who have been attracted by these few examples and want to know more will have no difficulty because unlike those of the rest of Africa, the recipes are at least recorded.

A book of Malay cooking by Hilda Gerber—who did a great deal for South African cooking in a short life—contains no less than two hundred Cape Malay recipes. I am compelled by lack of space, however, to concentrate on Malay dishes that are entrenched in the broader national idiom of contemporary South African cooking, conscious that I have left in the cold a rich world of brightly coloured sweet-meats, scores of puddings, biscuits and cakes like rainbows, fruit preserved in sugar and spice, unheard-of ways of doing despised forms of sea life like the squid, or sea-birds like bassiaan, the Cape hen or Mother Carey's chickens as the British sailors called them.

There are many kinds of atjar. I belief the first was the mango atjar as made in Java. Java to my mind is the greatest mango country in the world. Every district has its own variety and, in range and taste and texture, the Java mangoes rival those of India. I have eaten atjar there in a green form, pickled and tasting like a superior sort of Mediterranean olive or as an ingredient of a more complicated mixture with several kinds of chillies from the long and comparatively sweet Lombok to the aggressive little chubbi rawats. The first Cape Malay atjar too was a mango atjar differing from the Javanese in that it was dressed with oil and curry and carefully sliced from its stone. In its present forms, however, the fruit is taken just before the mangoes begin to turn. The flesh is sliced from the stone and left to lie in salt water for some days when the pieces are removed and dried. Some garlic and fenugreek, turmeric and chillies are cooked in oil, until the favourite curry powder combinations can be stirred into the mixture, which is then spread between layers of mango, arranged in classical order in a clean screw top jar. There must be enough hot oil to cover the mango, otherwise it will go bad. Lemons, green beans, onions, cauliflower and other kinds of vegetables were similarly turned into atjars but the greatest of all and the one most popular with the Europeans of the Cape and certainly the one that gave the most pleasure to us children in the interior was the mixed vegetable atjar which contained every kind of vegetable we could grow. This was really a massacre of the innocents because all the babes and sucklings of the vegetable kingdom went into it: tiny little cobs of maize, barely an inch in length, the youngest of cucumbers as soft and tender as they could possibly be, minute walnuts, the hearts of young cabbages, all manner of young beans, green, yellow and purple, the young flower of snow-white cauliflower, almonds, raisins, apricots, peaches, our special form of a thin, light skinned tangerine called nartjie, lemons, celery, tiny carrots, radishes, button turnips, in fact everything that the vegetable kingdom could offer.

Then there were the blatchangs. These also had their origin in Java—indeed they are still used there and acquired their name from the prawn and shrimp mixture that was used as part of Javanese sambals. The prawns and shrimps are dried in the sun, pounded in wooden mortars with several kinds of pepper and shaped into masses resembling large cheese. In this form blatchang arrived in the Cape where soon the prawns and shrimps were replaced by anchovies and, as well as the peppers, sliced gherkins and onions were worked into the mixture by the Malays who served it not as a cheese but preserved in tamarind juice and sugar or later in vinegar. From these beginnings the blatchangs evolved into more and more complex forms so that today we have not only these ingredients but blatchangs made from apricots, dates, quinces and raisins.

But the main interest of blatchang lies not in its sophisticated current complexities but in the fact that it became for South Africans what Worcester sauce or tomato ketchup became for the English. It followed them around from the Cape to as far north in the interior as Broken Hill in Zambia and even Eldoret in Kenya, and nowadays even pursues them abroad. I have bought a version of it in a grocer's shop in Aldeburgh in Suffolk.

As important as atjar and blatchangs in the life of the Malays were their sambals. They cover a far greater range in Javanese cooking which inspired them as I can vouch for from my own experience. But the point is that the Malays in the Cape quickly adapted the process to the nature of ingredients to which the Javanese never had access. For instance, the blatchang element which is incorporated in the Javanese sambal was quickly separated to become an independent art on its own and the Cape Malays restricted it to a condiment made of grated vegetables and fruits like carrots, cucumbers, apples and quinces. The grated ingredients were salted and seasoned either with fresh lemon juice or vinegar and the inevitable chillies. They used the same shredded vegetables as a salad, which we called "slaai", but the sambal was far more common and characteristic and no Malay curry or feast was complete without sambals of some kind. The quince sambal was a favourite with Malay roasts, from chicken to a leg of fat mutton, since it is a wonderful corrective to anything with a hint of grease or fat. Carrot sambal was a favourite with fried fish or roasted chicken and the apple variety a sort of Jack of all trades that went well with any dish. The Cape Malays were particularly good at pastries and they have made one contribution that is for ever a part of the mystique of South African taste—the "koeksister".

It is perhaps one of the most fattening pastries ever invented, and enough to make a waist-conscious dietician faint with horror. Yet when well done it is undeniably delicious. Hildagonda Duckitt's recipe, which she herself extracted from an old Dutch family cookery book going back to the eighteenth century, is a good example of a basic koeksister. Her ingredients are: three breakfast cups of flour, a teaspoonful of mixed spices, four well beaten eggs and a good tablespoonful of yeast. The yeast is dissolved and added to the ingredients made into a stiff dough with the whisked eggs, if necessary a little water or milk is added. The dough is left to stand for half an hour and rolled out on a pastry board. The rolled out pastry is then cut into strips about half an inch long which are dropped into a mixture of boiling fat and butter until deep brown, when they are extracted and dipped into a syrup made of three more cups of dark brown sugar and two of water, flavoured with cinnamon.

Finally there is the tameletje, whose role in the imagination of generations of South Africans of all races and colours demands that it should be the last word on Malay cooking, just as it was the first in most of our lives. It is a sweet brought to South Africa by the Malays and so old that nobody is quite certain of its origin. Specialists in these matters suspect it came from China where apparently sugar was first cultivated.

The basic ingredients are coarse brown sugar and water used in equal proportions. Some Malays will add dry ginger to the mixture, others cinnamon, crushed walnuts, almonds, peanuts and some even a little butter turning it into a rudimentary kind of marzipan. Tameletje used to be hawked round in the Cape by Malays who, for centuries, were a familiar sight among the white-walled and gabled houses set among vineyards and along avenues of oaks planted by the great Simon Van Der Stel in the seventeenth century. They were as familiar as the Malay fish hawkers who peddled their wares in ponycarts, blowing little trumpets which emitted plaintive, nursery-rhyme notes. The tameletje hawkers and their baskets, the fish sellers and the sound of their horns have all vanished and most of the houses of gable and grace gone to make of what was once the stateliest port of call in all Africa, an increasingly ugly concrete town. The tameletje has been overwhelmed by the avalanche of mass produced sweets available in the shops that now stand on every corner of city or village all over the peninsula. But I am certain that wherever there is a garden large enough to hide them and with wood enough to make a secret fire, little boys all over the country are still making the original tameletjes as we did as children. That was the beauty and attraction of the tameletje for us.

We did not need money to buy them from hawkers or from shops. We could make them for ourselves out of materials borrowed from the cooks. Permission to have sugar was often refused because sugar in my childhood was expensive, a great luxury and by no means the commonplace thing everyone takes for granted today. We children, hungering for something sweet in our harsh and austere lives in the interior had no hesitation in swiping sugar when the backs of its guardians were turned.

I became quite and expert at breaking into the store-house where our supplies of sugar and other precious things were kept under lock and key. I was so expert that I was never caught, although I am certain I must have been under constant and grave suspicion. Fortunately the gardens and orchards round our house were immense, covering many acres and containing sheltered copses where one could make a discreet fire without attracting attention from the big house.

Here we would make a syrup of our dark brown sugar and water in equal proportions, pour it into any old tin we could lay our hands on, make a quick fire between some flat stones, stand the tin upon it. We needed no expert like Hildagonda Duckitt to command us to boil the syrup briskly. Greed and a sense of guilt were imperious enough to make us hasten with our clandestine confection. As the mixture frothed and bubbled we would stir it with a wooden stick and in another tin full of cold water we would occasionally let a drop of the syrup fall from the stick into the water. The moment it congealed we knew the tameletje was ready. We would leave it, if we were brave enough, just a moment longer to let it caramelise a little, an alchemical touch incapable of definition or prescription. We could then pour it straight away into the cardboard lid of a box. The nearest I ever came to being caught was when I impulsively removed the lid of a cardboard box in which a new hat had just arrived for my eldest sister and ran off with it in order to answer a loud call for tameltje which had come up from the pit of my stomach, and those of my friends.

We had to disperse in a hurry when we saw the slim upright figure of my gentle sister coming down the long garden path, strangely resolute. But she was not coming in our direction because she herself had practised this art in her own childhood. The cardboard container was greased with some kind of fat—butter was far too great a luxury. The tameletje mixture would then be poured into the container. Miraculously it would set almost at once and we would be off to let it cool in safety. When ready, it was hard, translucent and, held against the African sun, glowed like the finest amber. Even in this simple form it never tasted the same twice because, made on an open fire in a garden, the wood smoke would impart a flavour to the sweet. And as we seldom used the same combination of woods twice there was always a new nuance to give its own atmospheric savour.

In the Cape, when I stayed with friends, we would make an elaborate form of tameletjie by culling pine cones from the dense forests. We would extract the seeds, pour a thin layer of tameletjie in the container, quickly sprinkle the pine seeds over the congealing mixture and then pour the rest of the tameltjie mixture into the box. But in the interior, our favourite form was to take in due season the stones of a special variety of apricots. We all grew apricots of many varieties. As children we grouped the varieties as firmly under two headings as modern psychologists group humanity under the two headings: introverts and extraverts. The extravert apricots were those with stones whose kernels were bitter and inedible. The introverts possessed stones, complaint and sweet and not only palatable but far more to our liking than shop-bought almonds. Nothing ever equalled these surreptitious, do-it-yourself tameletjies because they had incorporated deep within them the greatest of all spices, not to be found in any kitchen or pantry—the spice of first breaking with established practise and starting out on an adventure of one's own.

When I read Mark Twain, whom my father taught us to revere because he had met him on his visit to South Africa and loved his books, I am struck by the similarity of our lives to those of Huck Finn and Tom Sawyer and above all by a remark made to young Sawyer that "everything which a man *is* depends on what he puts inside him: a good cook's a king of men". I think immediately of the first tameletjie whose making I directed over a fire lost among the fig trees, heavy with purple fruit, at the bottom of our garden.

We have, in Afrikaans, words and expressions which live on to show the respect if not awe in which we once held the Cape Malays, however much our Government may reject them today. There is the strange Afrikaans word "Oorlaams" which I believe to be a corruption of a prefix "oer" denoting origin, combined with "Islan" —Moslem. We still use this word to describe any individuals particularly skilled, clever or gifted. We will say of an obviously talented person that he is thoroughly "oorlaams".

In my young days we also believed that the Malays could cure, with their own herbs and spices, diseases that our own doctors could not. The superstitious among us thought that the Malays were great magicians. There was a widespread conviction that they could "gool"—their word for the performance of magic deeds. For me, that magic was implicit in the revelation of my first taste of tameletjie.

CHAPTER SEVEN

The Dutch and French Go Colonial

THE Dutch East India Company, who founded the first settlement at the Cape of Good Hope in 1652, were determined that it should never be anything more than a kitchen garden or glorified farm. A breach was made in this firm intention by a small group of employees who deserted their service within a few years of the founding of the settlement, and, calling themselves "Free Burghers", set about the business of farming and becoming greengrocers on their own account. The Lord Seventeen, in Holland, went on doing their utmost to prevent the breach from widening but soon the Free Burghers had become so successful that more food was being grown at the Cape than the ships of the East India Company could buy. This local impetus towards transforming the settlement into a colony was finally brought about after the arrival of the Huguenots.

These French Protestants had fled from France much as the refugees of the Nazi terror in Germany and Austria in the thirties, to seek asylum in any country that could offer them freedom of conscience and religion, as in England and Holland. In fact, they arrived in Holland, already densely populated, in such numbers that they were a social embarrassment and the government of the day exerted some pressure on the reluctant Company to reduce the problem by giving them asylum at the Cape of Good Hope. The terms on which they were admitted to the Cape were harsh even for those days. For instance, although as fellow Protestants they were allowed to practise their religion freely, they were not allowed to establish French-speaking schools and the use of French was forbidden even in their churches. With Europe and France so far away, they quickly lost all external appearance of being French. Their language rapidly vanished from the scene, leaving a few odd philological remnants behind in the "kitchen language" rather like the broken columns on some hill in Greece which are all that is left to remind us of what was once a temple. I think, for instance, of certain oddities in Afrikaans pronounciation like the use of the French "r" which is still common in the areas where the Huguenots settled. There is the "ne", into which we have contracted the French "n'est-ce-pas" and use exactly in the same way, as well as certain words like "gepeupel"—a mob—which is clearly derived from the French "peuple" Above all, there are the great family names of South Africa which, although pronounced in Afrikaans in a way the Huguenot founders would not recognise, are still spelt in the original French way—Malherbe, du Plessis, du Toit, le Cleacq, Malan, Theron, de Villiers, Celliers, Hugo, la Buschangne, Taute, Olivier, de la Rey. Though the outward trappings of their French character quickly vanished and they took to their new homeland with an ardour and a commitment as great if not greater than that of the Free Burghers, the Huguenots made an incalculable contribution to the life and the character of the new colony.

I do not believe that the so-called Europeans of southern Africa could ever have developed so resolute and so tough a fibre as they did, had it not been for the presence of these men of conviction. One has only to compare the character of the colonials of the Cape with those of other communities founded by the Dutch, such as in Indonesia and the Caribbean where no Huguenot element was ever introduced, to see how compliant, even permissive their societies were compared to the fundamentally uncompromising, resolute, enterprising and independent nature of the Cape Settlers. In fact, from the moment the Free Burghers were joined by the Huguenots and their natural sense of grievance against Europe as personified by Louis XIV's France was added to that which the Free Burghers already had against the Lords Seventeen's Holland, the history of South Africa was set. It is a history dominated by the psychological distance between Europe and South Africa and increasing paradoxically, with almost geometrical progression, as the development of modern means of communication brings them physically nearer. The role of the French Huguenots in widening this profound split in the national character was of such overwhelming importance that one can tell from the way the mind of a fellow countryman works, whether the Huguenot proportion in his blood exceeds that of the Dutch.

If this was a book about the consequences of our national psychology in the history of southern Africa—a book that should be written—I would have much more to say, but all that is necessary here is to define and record this aspect of our beginnings as the greatest single factor in making life and food at the Cape the unique, gracious, generous, hospitable and world-renowned phenomenon it was so soon after its foundation and still is today.

One imagines that with founders of such staunch character, no matter what the difficulties of their physical and political circumstances, they would still have triumphed. But one must admit that they could not have picked on a place so naturally equipped to aid and abet their intent than the earth of the Cape and the well-watered valleys of the Hottentots-Holland range. Here they began to practise their husbandry as they had in Europe.

This explains why the influence of the sophisticated and complex art of Malay cooking was accepted in the first instance only in so far as it taught the new colonials how to overcome the one great deficiency in their own way of cooking: the art of preserving food in hot climates for long periods of time. It took several generations of contact with the Malays and the East before the Oriental contribution to South African cooking became an internal part of their lives and the spices of the East were no longer luxuries.

How different the story of cooking at the Cape of Good Hope was to that of the Dutch who colonised Sumatra, Java and the other islands of their Far East empire! There, the climate made European husbandry impossible. The compliant and permissive character of the settlers restricted their food to native dishes. On their rare visits to Holland, they sampled home fare with as much distaste as the food of the Cape, in spite of the fact that the rest of the world, including England and France and later Russia had begun to sing its praises. The historian Godee Molsbergen tells this significant story about the grand-daughter of the very van Riebeeck who founded Cape Town. She was born in Batavia in Java and on a visit to the Cape in 1709, only fifty-seven years after her grandfather's day, found the food so different from what she had been accustomed to in Java that she called it 'revolting' and kept on her Javanese slave as a cook throughout her stay at the Cape, instead of sending him back to his home as she had originally planned.

To interrupt so continuous a process as history with definite dates to mark where one trend ends and another begins must always be an arbitrary act. But, for me, the beginning of the Cape-Dutch-French way of life is the year 1685. It was not only the year of the

Revocation of the Edict of Nantes but the year in which perhaps the greatest of all the Governors appointed by John Company to rule at the Cape, Simon van der Stel, found that he loved the Cape more than his native Holland. He decided to live out the rest of his days there. He promptly persuaded a Commissioner sent out just then to the Cape by the Lords Seventeen, to grant him a large tract of land behind Devil's Peak on the eastern slopes of Table Mountain. This tract lay, well protected, in a wide and gentle curve, shallow and fertile and carved by time, wind and water out of the mountains of the peninsula. It had the advantage too of facing north, in the direction of the sun. Out of gratitude for this grant he called the beautiful homestead which he built on it, Groot, or Great, Constantia, after the daughter of the Commissioner. By 1699 when Van der Stel retired after governing the Cape with great imagination, resolution and independent judgement, Constantia was already acquiring fame in Europe. It expressed, in microcosm, the blending of French and Dutch into a new colonial culture. Van der Stel became the first gentleman farmer in the land and set a seal of respectability on the expansion of the garden settlement. From that day on, the Dutch word for farmer, "Boer", carried the highest social prestige. To be a "Boer" was the most aristocratic thing that one could be in colonial society at the Cape or for that matter, later on, in the interior, hence the name Boer Republics for Transvaal and Orange Free State.

Great Constantia was the model which, consciously or unconsciously, every budding or even established farmer did his utmost to copy. In the process, a new and extremely beautiful style of architecture called Cape Dutch was evolved with the gable as its central feature. The homestead at Constantia was one of the finest examples of this kind of architecture and was made more beautiful still as the years went by. So much had Van der Stel's imagination been committed to the Cape and its future possibilities that he was often quite unscrupulous in the ways he served it. Like his son, who succeeded him as governor, he shanghaid eminent architects and craftsmen. As a result, all sorts of greater or lesser Constantias rose all over the peninsula, and even further into the interior along the rivers and meadows folded away among the valleys and pleated earth to the north. The names they still bear are charged with the nostaligia of their founders like "Vergelegen" (situated far away), "Nooitgedacht" (would never have thought it), "Rustenburg" (fortress of rest), "Schoongesicht" (view of beauty), "Vrede-en-lust" (peace and contentment), "La Gratitude", one of the most beautiful of all, built in a valley called French Hoek (French Corner) after the Huguenots who settled there and one which sums up all in its name, "Banhoek"—the valley of exile.

More than providing the Cape with elegant houses filled with lovely furniture and beautiful things for the table, Simon Van Der Stel, by his own example, made certain that a great wine industry was established. Van Riebeeck had proved that grapes could be grown at the peninsula. On 2nd February, 1665, he obtained three gallons of grape juice from fruit grown at the Cape and devoted twice that number of lines in his terse, laconic official journal to celebrate the event. But it was really Simon Van Der Stel who, with the help of the Huguenots newly-arrived from the greatest wine producing country in the world, laid the foundations of the industry. More than two hundred years later the poet Kipling wrote "Under hot Constantia, broad the vineyards lie".

Van Der Stel's kitchen gardens and vineyards, according to a contemporary traveller, "equalled if not surpassed the celebrated gardens of France". Moreover his hospitality was as generous as he was magnanimous, and his entertainment was so lavish that the same traveller noted: "His publick table want not plenty either of European or African wines", and "All dishes and plates upon the board are made of massy—silver". A whole book could be written about the food and wine of Constantia—indeed it has been done repeatedly in Afrikaans—but all that is necessary here is to say that Constantia was the leading South African wine from early in the eighteenth century and had such a reputation in Europe that, when one of Miss Austen's young ladies fainted, no contemporary reader was surprised to learn that she was restored to her senses with a drop of "Constantia"; nor that Mrs. Jennings in *Sense and Sensibility* could announce: "I have just recollected that I have some of the finest Constantia wine ever tasted, so I have brought a glass of it for your sister. My poor husband, how fond he was of it! Whenever he had a touch of his colicky gout, he said that it did him more good than anything else in the world."

As a writer, I feel the highest recommendation of Constantia is that of Baudelaire. He was a guest at Constantia in its heyday under Hildagonda Duckitt's uncle. He was so carried away by the hospitality, the food and, above all, the wine, that he composed a poem containing the lines: " *Je prefere au constance à l'opium au nuits, L'elixir de ta bouche a l'amour se pavane.*" There are those indeed who believe that it was Baudelaire's experience at Constantia which was responsible for his attack on Brillat-Savarin, whom so many people all over the world regard as the ultimate authority on good taste in food and cooking, calling him among other things: "An inflated, ignorant, uncivilised, uneducated, inexperienced boaster who condemns himself out of his own mouth as somebody who knows nothing whatsoever about the holy science of cooking and the art of eating", because all the Savarin could say about wine in his book on the art of cooking was contained in the one sentence: "As far as wine is concerned, it is an invention of Noah and is made from the juice of the grape."

A time was to come when not only Constantia but all the wines produced at the Cape lost their reputation and world demand for them dropped to such an extent that it is a miracle the industry survived at all. There were many reasons for this, too many and complex to elaborate here. The point is, the industry survived and today has a greater reputation than ever before—a reputation that is still growing. This has been the result both of the extraordinary courage of the men who went on cultivating their vineyards despite all discouragement and of the fastidious attention paid by their sons to new methods of production.

One of the most redoubtable characters, one of the select few who led the Renaissance of wine-making at the Cape, was an American, William Charles Winshaw, born in Kentucky. He ran away from home at the age of eleven because he had a step-mother who was unusually cruel to him. Armed only with a Kentucky pumpkin pie, specially baked for him by his old Negro nanny, he fled from his home and started his series of incredible wanderings. He had a variety of jobs, working for a grocer who set him slicing bacon like a Dickensian waif at all hours of the day and night, loading and unloading ships in New Orleans, prospecting for gold; until one day, putting his last dollar on a horse called Mulligan, considered such a rank outsider that he got odds of a thousand to one, he won real money. The young boy then went south to Texas where he served in the Rangers until he made another fortune gambling and had enough to go to college to study medicine, becoming a doctor and eventually going to Germany to specialise in tropical diseases. Eventually he arrived at the Cape, doing heroic work in an outbreak of bubonic plague. He contracted the disease himself but characteristically refused to die, recovered, married his nurse, took to wine-making, rallying other growers into forming a great wine corporation. When I last heard of him he was still alive and vigorous though well into his nineties, and has a son who is following imaginatively in his footsteps.

The wine Renaissance began in the First World War, reaching fruition in the last, when so much of the world was cut off from the wine-producing countries of Europe and had to draw on South Africa and found how good the wines were. Since the South African soil has a singularly high sugar content, the breakthrough came first in wines of a high alcoholic content such as the sherry types and spirits like brandy. Some of the Cape brandies have as much character and flair as any to be found in the world. The sherries and brandies would be even more renowned had their reputation not suffered from the general disrepute into which all things South African have fallen as a result of the racial policies of the present government. South Africans themselves, of all races and colours, have become increasingly a wine-drinking people and wine is a valuable ingredient in cooking. Its role would perhaps have been greater were it not for the fact that the Malay cooks, who had such an influence, were Muslims whose religion forbade the use of any form of alcohol.

Yet at the Cape, Muslim law notwithstanding, the use of wine in cooking and its automatic appearance on the table was so constant and continuous that a young English sapper, on his way back to England from Madras in 1843, was amazed how much it was taken for granted even in boarding-houses. The quality of boarding-house wines was by no means negligible, as a story of Leipoldt illustrates. One of the most ordinary wines produced at the Cape was the famous Nagmaal wine. Nagmaal literally means 'night meal' but it is the Dutch word for the Last Supper and is the sacramental wine used on the four occasions a year when the Dutch Protestant churches of South Africa allow themselves Holy Communion. Leipoldt, who was something of a connoisseur of wine, tells how Bismarck, in gratitude for some Nagmaal wine presented to him by South African admirers, sent them in return a few bottles of Steinberger of the famous 1846 vintage. As a young boy Leipoldt drank some of the 1846. It was not to be compared, he declared, with the original Nagmaal product that had elicited Bismarck's gift. Leipoldt emphasises again and again the extent to which the cooks in his own young days used wine.

These two basic aspects of the original settlement at the Cape, first kitchen-gardening and then wine-making, determined the dominant pattern of husbandry. It is true that the original settlement also had the duty of providing company ships with fresh meat whenever possible, but animal husbandry never became the speciality that wine and market-gardening did. Meat, after all, could be preserved in brine; the dire necessity was for fresh vegetables, milk, butter and fruit to counteract scurvy, while wine was not only desirable for its own sake and the profits it soon produced as an export, but also as something to make the water tolerable. I have read in old Dutch accounts of voyages from Amsterdam to the Cape, how gradually the quality of the water in the best barrels would deteriorate until the quantity of maggots was almost as great as the water itself. The addition of wine was almost as necessary as fresh food at the end of a long voyage. Also, there were the Hottentots who kept cattle and fat-tailed sheep which they were occasionally prepared to barter. Parties of soldiers from Cape Town castle went regularly into the interior to forage for such supplies. The amount obtained in such a way was never very great and these factors must not obscure the extent to which the colonists also bred sheep, cattle, goats and horses. Nonetheless, meat never figured in the cooking of the Cape to the extent it did in the interior, except in Malayan dishes.

Strangely too, very little has come down to us that is original to the Cape in cooking game. Game was certainly abundant. The proof is that so many places in and around Cape Town are called after the wild animals that were first seen there. One of the earliest and loveliest houses in Cape Town was called "Leeuwenhof"—court of lions. There were large, portly hippopotamuses almost wading out to sea to welcome Van Riebeeck and his party when they landed, like municipal representatives of the teeming community of African wild life—so much so that the early colonists thought of them more as sea than land animals and called them sea-cows. There is no doubt that venison and wild-fowl figured prominently and happily in the diet at the Cape. But for the grand evolution of the art of cooking game and wild fowl, one has to follow the trail into the interior.

The French-Dutch contribution to Cape cooking accomplished

its greatest achievements in preparing fish and vegetables, apart from their expertise in cooking chickens. This last I am certain was purely a Huguenot contribution with its roots in the days when the great defender of the Huguenots, Henri of Navarre, declared it one of his intentions on becoming King of France to ensure that every citizen had a chicken in his pot on Sunday.

Another exception for which I believe the Huguenots were responsible was the delicious way the Cape cook had of preparing pork. The Malays, as Muslims, would rather have been keel-hauled than eat pork, but the new colonials quickly borrowed Malay methods and applied them to pork, even making pork sosaties, which many gourmets believe to be the highest point this particular dish can reach. "The basis, the corner stone of decent sosaties," Leipoldt declares unreservedly "is pork, not just any kind of pork. In these days we cut sosaties from any meat on which we can lay our hands, but on the old farms it was different. When a pig was butchered—which happened at least once a month since grand-father Hermaans was mad about pork—then they were very careful to cut the meat from underneath the ribs into long soft strips well marbled with fat in its texture but not too fat to make it greasy." They had a particular love of roasting it in baking pans or, best of all, grilling it on a spit in the open.

However, the first subject outside the vegetable kingdom to receive the serious attention of the French-Dutch colonial cook was fish. There is not only historic but poetic justice in this, because our aboriginal prototype, alas now vanished for ever, was a branch of the indomitable Bushman race called "Strand-Looper", meaning literally a "beach-walker" but idiomatically "beach-comber". The Strand-Looper lived entirely from the sea. All along the beaches of the Cape peninsula and along the rocky coast southeast towards the distant Cape Agulhas, the southern-most point of Africa, archaeologists have excavated huge mounds of shells, fishbones, oysters, mussels, and crustaceans. The Strand-Looper fell victim to the pastoral and more highly organised Hottentot who invaded his domain and when Van Riebeeck arrived at the Cape of Good Hope there were only a few miserable survivors living in the hills along the coast.

So, in concentrating on the produce of the sea, the new colonials merely continued the good work the Strand-Loopers had begun. But one of the most surprising things is that the French Huguenots, with such fine material on hand and knowing as they must have done all about the art, never produced a Cape version of bouillabaisse. Nor did they exploit the heritage of the hundred and more different French sauces of which Voltaire boasted. After all they could have drawn on the greatest range of sauces in the world from sauce tartare for fried fish to the incomparable sauce hollandaise for delicate poached or steamed dishes. Our own native sauces remain comparatively limited.

One favourite which deserves to be mentioned is a sauce made principally of Cape tomatoes, preferably fresh ones. These tomatoes of southern Africa, even more particularly those grown in the interior, deserve, even in parenthesis, a closer look. They are, I believe, the finest-tasting tomatoes in the world, particularly in the interior where they have had to fight the arid climate for survival. They are of several varieties, ranging from one which is almost a berry, hardly any bigger than the famous Cape gooseberries, to one of medium-size, elongated, fragrant to nose and palate and shaped like a rugby football, to the tomato the market gardeners of the Mediterranean have made familiar. They all have their different uses but share one supreme quality in that, like the people who grow them, they have a definite character of their own, with a fine, sharp assertive flavour. The tomatoes used for this particular fish sauce are of the Mediterranean type. They are skinned and finely sliced. About a quarter the number of onions as tomatoes are finely diced and browned in a little butter, the sliced tomatoes added, with a little pepper and salt, and allowed to simmer slowly until both onions and tomatoes are cooked, practically merged in one glowing, red sauce.

From this point onwards several variations follow according to the nature of the fish. If it is, say, grilled king-klip, which is one of the Cape's best fish, its nearest equivalent to turbot, wine is added to the basic tomato sauce. Some prefer dry white wine but I believe in the errant custom learned, I suspect, from the Portuguese who still observe it from Mozambique to Lisbon and Oporto. It is a custom that defines the established dogma of the French kitchen and its vast following of unenterprising lackeys. In the language of our time it would be called creative vandalism, for a dry red wine is used. But whatever the wine, the sauce has to be mixed with a white or brown roux, according to the colour of the wine, and left simmering long enough for the flour in the roux to be properly cooked. At this stage a certain amount of fresh lemon juice is added to the mixture because, judiciously employed, the lemon enhances the flavour of the tomato.

Then there are the curry and horse radish sauces. Horse radish sauce seems to have been naturalised at the Cape long before the coming of the English. In my youth it was grown even in the remote interior. There were many variations. One of our own favourites consisted of horse radishes fresh from the garden which were minced or grated. For every two tablespoonfuls of horse radish we added a medium sized peeled, cored and minced apple or better still, a ripe quince, similarly treated. Into this mixture, we stirred a little sugar, some wine-vinegar diluted to taste, salt and pepper, finishing it all by whipping in some fresh cream. This sauce went well with boiled, steamed or smoked fish. The more delicate the flavour of the fish the easier one went with the vinegar and the more generous one became with the cream. Some people added grated carrot to the sauce as well but this, I always thought, was, as we say in South Africa, like adding a fifth wheel to a wagon.

Good fish soups at the Cape were rare. It is only when we come to shellfish, starting with the lower orders like periwinkles and mussels, and going up the scale to the perlemoen and the incomparable crayfish that we encounter more enterprise. Periwinkles are good enough to eat raw but, like crayfish, they can be made into desirable ragouts. The better mussels were also made into powerful and tasty soups. In their case the stock was often made from milk and cream, spiced with nutmeg and flavoured with a sprinkling of grated cheese—a variation the Dutch loved so well that, as the breach with Holland widened, the colonists were re-baptised "cheese heads".

But the champion in this class was undoubtedly the perlemoen or abalone. This was and remains, although increasingly hard to come by, one of the great delicacies of the Cape kitchen. It is increasingly rare because it has to be dived for and nowadays tends to be canned and exported, mainly to the United States. It is a shellfish which even Hildagonda, whose pragmatic mind did not take wing in poetry, called "lovely, with a mother of pearl lining and most delicious if properly cooked". Used in the canned form of course, it is easy to handle; but freshly extracted from the sea it is a different matter.

It is immersed in cold water for about an hour before being

thoroughly scrubbed or curry-combed, particular care being taken to ensure that any green sea-fungus is removed. The perlemoen is then extracted from its shell, its beard shaved off, its innards removed and discarded. It is laid out on a block of wood and thoroughly beaten with a wooden mallet until the rather bony rind along its edges is soft and pliant. It is then put in a heavy pot with either a little butter or fat. But from here the ways for completing the dish divide. Hildagonda says all you have to do at this stage is to let it simmer for an hour or so, stir in a teacupful of fine bread-crumbs, two ounces of butter, some nutmeg and white pepper and, just before serving, a little salt. She warns also that it must occasion-ally be stirred carefully but that on no account must water be added, since the fish forms a rich gravy of its own, and she empha-sises that it requires lots of butter. In the final result it should be, she says, as tender as "a vegetable marrow". The reason the salt is added at the last moment is because if used earlier, it toughens the fish.

A peer of the perlemoen, is the Cape crayfish, one of the world's most delicious crustaceans, a statement proved, for those who accept the French as the final arbiters, by the fact that France buys them almost as fast as they can be canned at the Cape. Yet although the Malays recognised the potential of the crayfish early on, the new French-Dutch colonials virtually ignored it until the nineteenth century, from when it steadily became more popular until today it is cooked all over the country according to all the international recipes from Thermidor to Cardinal. Nonetheless it is significant that even Hildagonda, as late as 1891, limits herself to a single cray-fish recipe; the one for potted crayfish. That is fair enough, because potted crayfish was as distinguished a feature of a good kitchen as potted shrimps on toast are in Britain. Other pioneers like Mrs. Dykman, who preceded Hildagonda, and A. G. Hewitt, who followed her within a year or two of the first publication of her book, are hardly any better and seem content to follow the well-tried Malay examples of braising the crayfish with onions and chillies, or mincing it into the rissoles known all over the country as frikkedels.

Leipoldt recommends a recipe inherited from a lady who lived in the early nineteenth century in a valley deep in the Hottentots-Holland ranges. This lady would carefully extract the meat of young female crayfish from tail and claws, particularly the fatter flesh which lies against the shell, pound it fine in a mortar with the same amount of marrow extracted from the bones of beef and add some pepper, salt, breadcrumbs, the yoke of two eggs, a cup of whipped cream, a pinch of red chillies and a teaspoonful of fresh lemon juice. This mixture was re-inserted into the empty shells to be baked in an oven until done.

Spices are a vital feature of Cape cooking. From early in the eighteenth century, no colonial kitchen was considered well founded without a properly stocked spice cabinet. Most of them were preserved unground, so that they kept their freshness. Cinnamon, for instance, was always kept whole as bark; cloves, in what the "kitchen language" of the Cape termed, their 'needles'; nutmeg remained inviolate as a nut.

The extent to which these spices were still things of wonder to Europe and the colonials can be seen from the beauty of the original spice cabinets and the quality of the china of the jars in which they were preserved. The best of these came from Delft and were as clear and acute in their colour and as true in their proportions as objects extracted from an interior by Vermeer. These Delft jars alone are proof of how profound the effect of China and Japan had been on the awaking *nouveau riche* spirit of Holland. Much of the plate used at table too came either from the Far East or from Delft.

I remember, as a boy, walking along the shores of Table Bay when Cape Town was still a stately port and being amazed at the quality of the fragments of china thrown up on the yellow sands, no doubt pieces of the plate used in the saloons of some East Indiaman which had been sent to the bottom by the storms that blew up so suddenly in the wide but inadequately defended bay. This accounts for the manner in which ginger intruded more and more in Cape cooking as time wore on. The Chinese, with their finely differentiated taste in food, were dubious of the value of all spices and other fiery ingredients; but they made a significant exception of ginger. This exception was due more to a kind of religious superstition than to a deliberate matter of taste. The "gin", from which the word ginger is derived, is the European pronunciation of the Chinese word for "man". The root from which it is made is a form of the famous "gin-seng" of Chinese history, literally "man-root", so-called because it is shaped like the Chinese character for "man". It was supposed to have the quality of prolonging life indefinitely. It was valued most in its wildest form, and so much sought after that China produced special wild gin-seng hunters who penetrated far up the Pacific coast hunting for it in the dense forests of Siberia. Somehow all the importance the Chinese attached to the presence of ginger in their food imparted itself to the Dutch of the Far East without involving the superstition to the same extent.

I can still remember the excitement we experienced in the interior when boxes of groceries arrived and we all stood around, breathless, waiting for the jars of willow-pattern Chinese porcelain to appear and reassure us that we would have our favourite preserved ginger and fresh cream as a pudding that night. The original jars in which the first ginger arrived at the Cape were such things of beauty in themselves that they were preserved in many households like my own and stand today on the dark old Cape Dutch furniture as flowerpots of the most graceful kind. I find it a little sad therefore to have to record that our love of ginger came to exceed the law of proportions so perfectly expressed in the jars which contained it. It is used far too indiscriminately in certain aspects of our cooking. For instance, it is unthinkingly and automatically inserted into our incomparable South African jams so that the superb flavour of the fruit is compelled to kow-tow to the totalitarian taste of Chinese ginger.

I have therefore taken care in all I say about Cape Dutch cooking to avoid it where I think its presence is more harmful than good. The same applies to all our other spices and only some generalised observations about their use are necessary here. We believe that cinnamon improves all fruit dishes from the humble stewed varieties to the more elaborate pies, tarts, and fools. We use it, ground, with roast pumpkin, sweet potatoes, pancakes and in cakes and biscuits. We find that nutmeg, freshly grated on buttered new potatoes supports their delicate flavour. We believe nutmeg goes well with marrow and, in moderation, in egg dishes of all kinds. We use cloves not only for hams and baked apples but also to stud roast legs of mutton, roast venison and all forms of jugged game. We believe that rice is better for the addition of turmeric and saffron.

There remain two other forms of the Cape cook's expertise to discuss: his methods with fowl and pork. Chicken was a great favourite on Sundays when the main meal was eaten after church in the middle of the day. The most exalted form was a chicken pot-roasted with a few slices of bacon, its juices sealed within the skin by a light browning before a little dry white wine was added. The

lid was firmly jammed in position on the heavy cast-iron pot—
aluminium will just not do—to prevent any moisture from escaping
while the fowl was roasted for about an hour and a half.

This chicken could be done with what the English call the "usual
stuffing" but the best Cape way and, to my mind, the perfect one,
was to stuff it with grapes of the variety we call "Hanepoort"—
literally "cock's foot". The South African English call this grape
"Honey pot" but, in reality, its remote ancestry can be traced to the
species the French call *Muscat d'Alexandrie*. It is one of the great
grapes of the world. Simply as a fruit it has a most delicate aromatic
flavour, redolent with an indefinable scent like the petals of the
finest flowers of Persia. It makes wines of a velvet texture and warm
amber in colour such as Constantia Berg. It is superb as a raisin
and first-rate as jam.

Whenever I ate chicken cooked this way in some old Huguenot
house at the Cape I experienced the strange sense of living history
that a good dish should produce in one; a feeling that somewhere
out in the wings of time the spirit of Henri of Navarre, who embodied
Sunday roast chicken in law, would rest easier for seeing it spread
so far and wide as this Southern Cape.

Last of all there is pork. I will concentrate on only one of the
many forms in which the best cooks at the Cape prepared it for
great occasions. I speak of the roast suckling pig, one of the delicacies
of European cooking. The foremost French gourmets like Brillat-
Savarin—despite Baudelaire—would show their reverence for the
sucklings, by decorating them with colourful ribbons and shining
paper cut in delicate patterns. There is even a story told of a great
French nobleman who loved the dish so much that, on his rare
excursions into the country, he never passed a clutch of suckling
pigs without formally raising his hat to them. At the Cape too the
suckling pig was prepared with the utmost reverence. When it had
been cleaned, scraped and scrubbed again and again in boiling
water it was rubbed down until dry. There was no question of
dusting, even with the finest flour. Our cooks would quarrel a great
deal about what sort of stuffing was best. Yet even in this matter
they tended to be purists and so great was their faith in their
material that they often let the tender taste go into the world of the
table unaided and alone. Their one concession, assuming it was a
suckling in good condition, would be to rub the skin with fresh
lemon, a corrective to fat, and of course salt and pepper. They

would then proceed to the roasting in a baking pan, resorting to
constant basting until the animal's skin was dry and crackling like
static electricity at the touch of a probing fork. This dish went best
with rice or sweet potatoes cooked in their jackets. Failing these,
some ordinary potatoes, also baked in their jackets were good
substitutes but above all a good, tart quince jelly was a must.

Most of all, I loved suckling grilled, however primitively, in the
open over charcoal heaped with wild mountain herbs to impart,
through their smoke, a Pan-like savour to the meat of the young
animal. One of my earliest memories indeed is of eating such a pig
on a farm in the Valley of Exile served with a quince sauce and the
finest of young turnips, hardly bigger than the average button,
braised in a little white wine and butter. I never knew where this
idea of combining turnip and pork came from, because I had
encountered it only at the Cape, until many years later, in a small
restaurant lost in the great Forêts du Dom in the south of France,
I ate wild boar with only this vegetable accompaniment. I saw then
that a root should go well with the progeny of an animal which
itself is such an expert at rooting and with so much of the nature of
the root incorporated in its being through its love of the tubers of
the earth. I should have known that only the French or the Chinese
could have fastened on so felicitous a coincidence.

It may seem paradoxical that in a colony which started as a
kitchen garden and developed market gardening on such a vast
scale as the Cape that I have said so little about their way of cooking
vegetables. This is a deliberate omission because I think in the
interior, although rooted in the Cape tradition, we not only cooked
vegetables as well if not better but also that the same vegetables
there had more flavour. There is a mysterious element in nature,
almost a kind of Cinderella magic within the earth, which decrees
that the harsher the environment and the more desert-like the
climate, the sweeter the fruit when the rain falls to quicken it. I
have been amazed, for instance, in the deserts of the world, particularly in the Kalahari, how, when the rain falls, it suddenly produces
wild cucumbers, flowers of an Arabian Nights brilliance, melons,
natural equivalents of plums, apricots and shrub berries so sweet
that game from more privileged areas move in their hundreds and
thousands to make a feast of such unusually delicate and sweet fare.
Elephants adore these desert fruits because they are devout vege-
tarians and great gourmets, and it has always been difficult for me

to decide which have the better taste in these matters: elephants or baboons, but judging by the distance they still travel and the trouble they will take, elephants perhaps are top of the class. I have caught them in the Kalahari desert almost like naughty schoolboys in the act of retreating from a raid on a well-stocked larder, slinking away from a rich grove of wild plums, so full that they had gripes and seemed to be clasping at their stomachs with their trunks as if in acute pain. They have the sweetest of teeth and if one remembers how long their teeth are one will know how great a love of sweetness they must hold.

The climate of the Cape, in comparison with that of the interior was just a little too lush, access to water in the soil was too easy, so that the fruit and vegetables tended to be somewhat soft and easy-going in character and so deprived of the finest edge of their flavour. Also, the Cape had so much of everything, such a rich choice in this regard, that the people placed little value on their produce. In the interior we were so severely rationed that we were compelled to make the most of all our material, though we owed many of our methods originally to the Cape.

Some years ago, walking with a friend of mine through one of the oldest wine and fruit farms, established by his ancestors at the Cape nearly three centuries ago, I was amazed all over again to note how well the founders of the colony had planned their fruit and vegetable economy. They had planted, for instance, so that the first apricots would appear in the spring. After the austerities of winter, this fruit, turning yellow, glowing among the leaves like the immortal arbouse of the Mediterranean whose shrub, bowed low with fruit, lights up the background of many a beautiful European primitive painting of the Nativity, would seduce us as schoolboys into raiding the orchards so avidly that, like the elephants in the Kalahari, we all slunk away, suffering from a well-known indisposition called "apricot tummy". From then on almost into the autumn, the apricot was followed by other varieties of its kind, maturing later and later. By Christmas the plums—and Chinese plums were among the great favourites—balanced the hunger for apricots and, almost at the same time, the first crop of figs, more plums and peaches, not to mention grapes, appeared in ordered succession, to be followed at the first hint of autumn by quinces and pomegranates which could be stored in gabled attics almost indefinitely. In winter, the orange and naartjie took over after a seasonal twilight glow of medlars and the

Oriental persimmon, and, helped by the amber loquat and the guava, filled in the gaps in the annual cavalcade of fruit. The guava, sliced open, was rich with the colours of a still-life by Gauguin. Its jams, jellies and bottled forms were exciting elements in Cape foods. Peeled and sliced it was a quintessential ingredient of angel's food and other fruit salads. Also there were the sweet melons, the musk melons, the water melons and winter melons, and even, at times, strawberries from the hills, above all from the slopes of the hills around Stellenbosch, called after Simon Van Der Stel. On hot summer's days in the streets of Cape Town, the coloured hawkers of the city carried these strawberries around in great baskets. The berries themselves were packed in smaller baskets, tenderly tucked in between quilts of oak leaves whose scents would pervade them with the utmost felicity.

A special word about the grapes of the Cape is necessary. It has always amazed me how inferior are the grapes offered as fruit in the great wine-producing countries of Europe. On the Continent they appear on stalls and in households almost as an afterthought and when they are grown specially for the table as they are in Belgium, Holland and Britain, which are not wine-producing countries after all, they may look beautiful but their taste is as cloistered, confined and anonymous as the glass conservatories, the vegetable nunneries, in which they have been raised. But in the Cape and all over southern Africa the grape is prized not only for its great wine-making potential but is grown as much for eating as for curing as raisins or making jam. Not surprisingly, as a fruit it has established almost a monopoly of the market in Great Britain for five months of the year. Even so, apart from the exploitation of its export potential, the best grapes for eating and for jams are to be found in the interior. From the point of view of cooking, however, there are some fruits so uniquely of the Cape that they must be dealt with here. I think, for example, of Cape gooseberries, apricots, guavas and loquats and the role they play in tarts, pies and cakes.

The Cape gooseberry almost deserves a chapter to itself. It is not a native of the Cape as its botanical name *Physalis Peruvina* clearly demonstrates. It came to us, according to an old legend in my own family who always took a great interest in these things, not from Peru but by way of the Crimea in one of the Russian ships which, as time went on, became frequent callers in Table Bay. When ripe, it is a green-gold berry contained in a straw-coloured hood or as the "kitchen language" had it, a "kappie", that is, a little sun-bonnet. All refined tastes in fruit, I think, are highly ambivalent and a Cape gooseberry combines tartness and sweetness, creating a tension that stimulates the palate. Apart from making delicate tarts or summer puddings, it can be used, if enough care is taken not to make it too sweet, as an accompaniment to roasts. But to us it is most popular as a jam, not in the mass-produced form that so damages its reputation in the world outside but as we made it at home in the Cape. The grape jams of the Cape, too, when home-made, were exceptional either in the jelly or the whole-fruit form. But perhaps the greatest honour should go to the naartjie, the Cape form of tangerine with its thin, closely fitting skin of citrus satin. It was as great a favourite of grown-ups as children and the special delight of all those who called in at the Cape. It is to the Cape what the kum-quat—a member of the citrus family too—is to China, and I have an instinctive conviction that the Cape recipes for the naartjie are a local application of good kum-quat principles from China.

The main reason why Cape jams were so varied and so good was because the process was all part of the initial incentive that had brought the Cape colony into being: that of providing men with food that would keep for long under almost impossible conditions. A vast industry developed which still exists and is expanding.

There are one or two delightful versions of preservation unique to the Cape, among them, mebos. This was a method of an almost childish simplicity as perhaps the best inventions are, though I cannot be sure how much of my judgement is due to childhood associations, which play so profound and so unrecognised a role in matters of taste. I add this reservation because mebos was undoubtedly among the greatest favourites of South African children of my generation. Mebos is made out of soft ripe apricots immersed in salt water for some four hours. The apricots are extracted and spread on the clean rush-mats to dry in the sun. After one day they are flattened between the palms of the hand to let the stones gently emerge. The flattening process was generally repeated each day and if the weather remained good the mebos, depending on the strength of the sun, would be complete in between three to four days. But if the weather turned damp the mebos could be dried off in a heated room or in a very low oven. The apricot thus dried would then be dipped for some five minutes in lime water prepared by boiling two tablespoons of fine lime in a quart of water. Lime water was used a great deal in making preserves and jams out of all fruits, particularly any in their greener states with a high acid content. Immersed in this liquid, the apricots were taken out as soon as they began to feel tender, dried on a soft cloth and coarse crystallised sugar carefully rubbed into each apricot. The apricots were preserved in well-sealed jars and kept thus to lighten the darkness on our palates caused by the absence of fresh fruit in the winter. In the eyes of the sea-conscious colonists of the Cape, they had the additional virtue of being considered an infallable remedy for sea-sickness—a complication of function which we as children were mercifully spared in our land-locked interior, because heaven knows what schizoid conflicts might have broken out if we had had to think of this delightful substance as medicine as well!

Some of the subtlest preserving syrups and sweetening mediums peculiar to the Cape have alas vanished, and others nearly so. I think above all the syrup of the unique Cape flower: the protea In Afrikaans it is called the "suikerbossie"—a little sugar bush—for reasons I expect few if any of the people who use the name today know. It was called thus because in the early days at the Cape the inhabitants would send their Malay slaves and coloured servants out into the hills annually to collect the sweet juice which lay in the bottom of the flower's bell. The process was known as to "skud", that is to "shake" the protea. The juice was called "bossiesstroop" (little bush syrup). It was of a bright, pale yellow colour and was strained through muslin and boiled in sugar, often with a stick of cinnamon included. On sweet omelettes, baked eggs or pumpkin fritters it was regarded as a most especial treat, because it took a great many flowers to make a single bottle of syrup.

No matter how far back in our history one searches, and I think I have searched as far as most, rice figured in the pride of place in the food of the Cape, although it has never been grown there. No South African household will consider a meal complete unless it is accompanied by rice of some kind. Moreover, in the Cape colony, as among Boers of the interior, one was normally offered both rice and potatoes at dinner. The rice, of course, is cooked in many different ways and has innumerable sophists of the palate who quarrel incessantly over almost invisible distinctions in a way that would shame a British trade-unionist's metaphysical capacity for disputing lines of demarcation. To my mind, there is no doubt that the best method is the original one acquired by the first servants of

John Company at the beginning of the seventeenth century in the East. It was simply to pour carefully selected grains of rice into double the quantity of boiling salt water. As soon as the rice began to soften slightly, it was strained through a sieve into another saucepan so that the water could be preserved. The rice itself was then rinsed under a cold tap several times, placed in a steamer which fitted tightly into the saucepan containing the water. The steamer was also covered with a tight-fitting lid and put back on the fire to steam for another twenty minutes, when usually it would be not only thoroughly reheated but of a delicious and paradoxically wet kind of dryness as well.

There is a method of preparing cabbage that is unique to the Cape. Traditionally, this requires a firm young cabbage which is cut into slices about three-quarters of an inch thick, placed in a deep dish on a generous layer of bacon and the dish filled on this foundation with alternate layers of cabbage and bacon, sealed on top with a couple of rashers. The rashers should have their rinds removed. The dish, which should be a heavy one, has its lid tightly clamped down and is put into a moderate oven until the cabbage turns a light green-gold in colour. It is then extracted and the lid removed so that the top rasher can be finished off under a grill. This rich dish has such a reputation that it gave Afrikaans a unique expression: "kool sonder spek", that is cabbage without bacon, a term used to describe anything, be it person or idea, lacking in character or flavour.

Uniquely of the Cape too, is the penguin's egg. The cold Antarctic current annually brings penguins to nest on the rocks and islands in and about the Cape. It did not take the food-conscious Dutch of John Company long to discover what an excellent delicacy penguins' eggs were. They collected eggs in their thousands and although they were not unusual in my youth at the Cape I never realised the passion they aroused in colonial palates at the beginning, until searching through South African archives I found recipes for making even omelettes out of penguins' eggs for whole families—and Cape families were as large as their appetites. In my youth, however, the penguin population was in some danger of extinction and one considered oneself lucky to be offered in due season a penguin's egg as an *hors d'oeuvres* once or, at the most, twice a week. Today the Government, quite rightly, has severely limited the number of eggs allowed to be collected for sale to private individuals. People who love them have to watch the newspapers for a Government announcement inviting them to send whatever the market price may be to an appropriate official address and the penguin gourmet if he is lucky, will receive a case containing two dozen eggs at most, or his money back.

There are many schools of thought as to how so rare a dish can be made to give of its best. The classical way is to boil the eggs for at least twenty minutes. They must then be removed from their shells quickly so that they do not lose any of their heat; I have known penguin-egg lovers who keep special gloves for the purpose. The extracted egg, burning hot, is dropped in a hot tumbler, mashed quickly with a fork in fresh butter, a little pepper, salt, and sometimes a drop or two of wine vinegar or lemon. It is then whisked quickly into a sort of soufflé consistency. I have eaten it also cold, at an hotel which specialised in penguins' eggs and stood almost in the surf on Blueberg Strand with a superb view over the bay towards Devil's Peak, Table Mountain, Signal Hill and Lion's Head. There, the mildest of salad dressings was served with the cold eggs and the result was good, but the egg is best left to itself except for butter and salt and a trace of pepper. Coming as it does from one of the oldest forms of life it has a savour so remote and tenuous that it must not be corrupted by modern substances. Moreover there is nothing at all fishy in the taste of the penguin egg. It is far, far superior to any of the plover or gulls eggs so popular as an *hors d'oeuvres* in parts of Western Europe. I prefer it even to caviare.

One other branch of cooking in which the colonists of the Cape achieved the highest distinction and perhaps continue to lead the rest of South Africa was in the baking of breads, cakes, biscuits, tarts and pastries in a formidable variety. It still amazes me how the earliest books on cookery available in our archives devote the major portions to the arts of baking. It is almost as if the cooking of meat, fish and vegetables was either so inborn or learned from so early an age that it could be taken for granted, but that in baking everyone sought guidance, new points of departure and constant variations of well-established themes. In this the Malays, who invented the "koeksisters" and had a Persian love of delicate pastries, matched and reinforced the love of baking that both Dutch and French brought with them from Europe. The American "cookies"—a word the United States owes to the Dutch of New Amsterdam—were developed there with no greater fervour and invention than at the Cape. One sub-species alone, the "soet-koekie", sweet cookie, had almost as many descendants as Jacob had sons of Israel and although Hildagonda gives only one recipe to represent this branch of a great chosen race I suspect it was because she despaired of giving them all.

Writers like Mrs. Dykman, who were less under English and European influence than Hildagonda, were not nearly so restrained. They had so many cookies, cakes, pastries and puddings that they ran out of names for them and were compelled to call them after national events or adjectives associated with historical occasions like "Voortrekker" (covered wagon pioneer), "Bond", which means "union" and refers to the first great political party formed at the Cape to reconcile the conflicting English and Dutch of the colony, "Jings cookies", after the imperialistic treaty of Cecil Rhodes and so on down to homely descriptions like ginger, cinnamon, auntie's, old batchelor's, spinster's, "snatched kisses", railway, pound, patriot's, until finally the adjectives run out and a cookie appears under the pseudonym of "Mrs. D's" cookie. With such an *embarras de richesse* it is not surprising that Leipoldt, in his two important works on food, refused to have anything to do with this department of the kitchen, although in the manner of our day he had no difficulty in finding noble reasons for ignoble evasion. I frankly feel compelled to follow the coward's way and abide by Hildagonda's example.

This profusion of baked delicacies was possible because, early on in their history, the colonists discovered a great stretch of black earth near the site of what is now the thriving country town of Malmesbury. The earth was as dark as the famous Bible-black earth of Russia and as fertile for growing wheat as any land in the Ukraine. Indeed it is significant that, as contact with Russian ships increased, several breeds of wheat were imported from the Ukraine on the premise that if they could withstand the extremes of cold, heat and drought of the Ukraine, they would do well at Malmesbury, which suffered from similar extremes, bitter winters and long, rainless summers with heat so intense that the air in the fertile valleys seemed to run like molten glass. Even on the high plateaux, the highveld of the interior, we found the best grain was a Russian variety called Dkurum which not only defied all our own extremes of climate but provided flour for the loftiest of cakes and lowliest of cookies.

The Cape therefore had all the material for encouraging the art of baking from early on and I know of no colony which cultivated it so diligently and so well. For me, the position of absolute command in this area of the national kitchen is occupied by something we call the "mosbollietjie". We owe it entirely to the Cape, particularly its French-Huguenot element. "Mos" is the name for the juice of the grape in the first stage of fermentation and "bollietjie", a diminutive as well as a form of endearment of the Dutch word "bol" which literally means a sphere or ball, but in this context denotes a bun.

To this day I am quite incapable of saying which of the two features of mosbollietjies I found most exhilarating; the sight of them coming out of the oven, a deep dark brown like that of Attic honey; or their smell which immediately spread out through the kitchen and pantry to fill the atmosphere of our nursery tea-room like some kind of invisible but highly aromatic smoke. We ate them warm, with the fresh butter, either with tea or coffee on a cold winter's afternoon and we thought there could be nothing more appetising in the bleak, wide world. But that was not the end of the enormous service mosbollietjies performed for us, because all that were left over were promptly cut in half and placed upside-down in a baking pan, and baked into the brown rusks we call "mos-beskuit" a word obviously derived from the French Huguenot "biscuit"—twice baked.

Out of this concept of baking grew the national phenomenon called "boere-beskuit" which played such an enormous role in the history of the interior. But it was "mos-beskuit" which was responsible for introducing us to the French fashion of breaking our fast with a Cape form of petit-dejeuner: a cup of hot coffee and milk and a small plate of mos-beskuit, usually brought to our bedside just as the fierce impatient day of Africa broke. We would eat the hard biscuit just as the French peasants will do their stale or twice-baked bread in the provinces of France, dunked first in the hot coffee and swallowed with sips of the hot liquid in between. If there is a better way of beginning a hard working day, I would like to know of it.

Other, humbler Cape pastries were "oblietjies" or "oublies" as they were called in the Huguenot valleys in my childhood. It is known that the Huguenots brought the recipe to the Cape but why they carry this evocative name is not precisely known, although it provokes all kinds of nostalgic speculation, because the origin would appear to be the French word for forgetting—"oublier". This might imply either that they are of such antiquity that their beginning is forgotten or again that they who brought them to the Cape were, in a sense, a people forgotten by the country of their origin; or, as Hilda's biographer suggests, because their dark colour recalled the *oubliettes*, the dungeons of France, in which many a Protestant had been imprisoned.

This would be the point at which to mention the great role the waffle played in Cape kitchens. Waffles originated in the Low Countries. They were indeed brought by the Dutch to New Amsterdam and so became naturalised Americans, but to this day I have not eaten better waffles than in the Low Countries, particularly in Flanders. In the beautifully preserved city of Bruges, for instance, on many a wet and cold occasion I have been served with such light, delicious and heart-warming waffles that my mouth waters at the memory. In my youth all Afrikaans or Boer coffee houses in the cities served waffles with coffee for elevenses. They were eaten with syrup. Any kind was suitable but for me there was nothing so good as South Africa's own equivalent of maple syrup: "moskonfyt". Moskonfyt, like almost everything else at the Cape, was produced with a great many variations. It was made in the huge coppers that every well-conditioned farm in South Africa had in its courtyard near the kitchen for making soap. Into this pot, the natural unfermented juice of crushed grapes was poured. Some people added metabisulphate and lime to prevent the juice from fermenting because if due care was not taken, as I found to my cost as a child, one could get rather tipsy on a confection unexpectedly intoxicating. This addition, incidentally, is a precaution recommended by an authority like Mrs. Malherbe who had her recipe straight from her Huguenot ancestors. But in reality the confection could be perfectly well made without it. The juice was heated in the pot and as it started bubbling and foaming, the impurities, rising to the surface, were constantly scummed. For as long as the juice was kept on the boil, continuous dipping and pouring with a ladle or scoop was necessary to prevent the juice both from boiling over and burning. The process was continuous until the juice had turned into a brown liquid, with a sugar content of approximately seventy per cent. Some connoisseurs, with the instinctive distrust all good cooks have of the effect of steel on delicate substances, would make their ladles out of broomsticks with a gourd fastened to the end.

When the moskonfyt was ready, it was allowed to cool until luke-warm and then poured still liquid, into bottles.

I have described the preparation of moskonfyt because, just as the tamaletjie had to conclude the story of Malay cooking at the Cape, since it was the oldest theme in their repertoire, moskonfyt is not only oldest in the kitchens of the colonial French-Dutch but older by far even than tameletjie, if not the oldest recorded of all European recipes accessible to us in the world today.

Just how old it is struck me with renewed force when I went back to Bamhoek, the Valley of Exile, which I mentioned at the beginning of this chapter. I went back for many reasons but above all because for my own family, unlike most of the people who live in it, it is a place of double exile. Not only did my ancestors on my mother's side settle near there, as exiles, but after the Anglo-Boer war of 1899–1902, my own father was exiled from the Orange Free State and my family lived for some years in a house very near to it. My father was exiled because he was the chairman of the last executive council of the last Parliament of the Republic of the Orange Free State which had just been defeated with its ally, the Republic of the Transvaal in their three years' war against the English. My father was not only a statesman but a fighting Boer commandant as well. When the war ended he smarted so much over the injustices of annexation that he refused to take the oath of alliegance to the British. Fearing his influence, the British sent us into what was a second exile. I remembered all this and more as I watched the beautiful valley and Delft-blue mountains in the lovely light of an early autumn. I remembered how I had once read Virgil's Georgics in this very setting. He himself had written them at the command of Caesar Augustus because, as in my father's day, war, the commandeering of farmers and the disintegration of the Roman spirit had reduced agriculture in Italy to a mess, and both Augustus and his friend Maecenas believed that Virgil, who so loved the land, could put new heart into his countrymen by writing his Georgics. I remembered being profoundly moved by his description of how the Roman farmers ploughed with oxen, irrigated the parched fields, burned the Italian veld at night to make way for the new grass in the spring, studied the ways of the bees, described the many precepts for the care of vines, pruning of fruit trees and the sowing of wheat, just as the farmers were growing and setting about all these things in the country round about me. In the light of all these parallels in what I have from the beginning called this strangely Mediterranean-like part of Africa, the valley settlements looked infinitely older to me than their three hundred years.

I never again forgot this aspect of Virgil in the context of the universe he created in poetry. Later when working on the Cape newspaper, the *Cape Times*, during the year that the two thousandth anniversary of Virgil's birth occurred, I commissioned a young Afrikrans Classical scholar of the day called T. J. Haarhoff to write a series of special articles on Virgil and printed them on the leader-page, which was in my special charge. I headed the first article of the series: "How Virgil described the making of Moskonfyt two thousand years ago."

I can do no better than let the relevant piece from this series say the last word on moskonfyt and all that it conveys of the deeper meanings implicit in the art of cooking and its place in civilisation. The quotation refers to the cottage scene in the first book of the Georgics where the wife of the Roman husbandman sings as she works and goes on to boil on the fire sweet grape juice, scumming the surface of the bubbling copper cauldron with leaves. Many commentators were puzzled by this until Haarhoff stumbled on the explanation. One eminent commentator had wrongly described it as just another method of making wine. Ramsey in his book on Roman Antiquity spoke of the produce thus rendered as a sort of jelly.

"But to us who have grown up at the Cape," Haarhoff wrote, "it is all familiar. The long continued boiling of the grape juice to about a quarter of its bulk (or as Pliny says, one-third), the forming of the scum that has to be removed from time to time, even the detail of the copper cauldron—we know it all, as the method of making moskonfyt, which is Latin in form as well as in substance, for it is simply '*mustum et confectum*'."

CHAPTER EIGHT

Food on the March

THE governors of the Cape, looking with a disapproving eye at
their settlement spreading out across the flats and into the
valleys of the mountain range beyond, thought of the new part of
their inflated parish as a "boland" highland—and called the people
living in it "bolanders"—highlanders—as they are known to this
day. This term, however, was and is extremely misleading. These
imposing mountains were really nothing but the eroded fragments
of the escarpment on the edge of the real highlands of southern
Africa: a vast plateau covering most of Africa all the way up north,
almost to the fringes of the Sahara desert. To people like myself
born on this plateau—we call it highveld—it was strange to think
of the people down *below* at the Cape as Bolanders. However, we
had come to the highveld too late to change such things even had
we so wished. So late was it in the history of the colony that my own
grandmother, her sister and brother took part as young children in
the great covered-wagon exodus we call the Great Trek. They were
in fact, with their Cape-coloured nurse, the only survivors of one
of the first columns of wagons to break into the interior. My great-
grandfather and the rest of the party was massacred by the Matabele
almost on the banks of the Vaal river at dawn one morning in 1835.

The reasons why the colony spilt over into the interior so late in
the day are too many and complex to be described in detail but one
obvious one was that it was much easier to follow the line of the
valleys and the fertile, well-watered routes along the East coast
northwards than to force a way across the formidable mountains
into the true highlands of southern Africa. Another was that even
on this limited course of expansion some eighty years after Van
Riebeeck's landing, the colonists collided head-on with a vast tide
of Bantu peoples slowly making their way south. A long series of
official and unofficial wars followed, often reminiscent of the clash

of the American frontier men with the Red Indian nations. The final incentive to break through the barrier of mountains and invade the unknown and dangerous interior beyond was really another product of the sense of growing psychological estrangement. Great numbers of colonists, mostly of Huguenot-Dutch descent, decided they had had enough of Europe as personified by British administration at the Cape.

I think here of the wild geese I have often watched apparently placidly afloat on some flashing hippopotamus water in the heart of Africa, as still as painted geese on a painted pool, looking as if they would be there for ever and unaware that some strange invisible charge was building up within them so that suddenly, without even a honk, just as if some common electrical current had conveyed an urgent warning, they would all take wing together and vanish over the bush into the blue. Something of this nature happened in the collective unconscious of the French-Dutch colonists on the exposed and war-ravished frontiers of the colony. One day they piled up their long covered wagons with all the provisions and goods they could hold, hitched them to their teams of oxen, put their women in the driving seats with their children beside them, mounted their horses, gathered their cattle, left their well-established farms and comfortable homes behind them and abandoned the colonial Cape for ever.

Yet just as the French and Dutch exiles had made the Cape a fertile and civilised colony on the pattern of the European culture they had abandoned and which had abandoned them, in the interior men took the memory of what was good in the way of life of the Cape along with them and in the process, in new and grimmer circumstances, evolved something more robust and authentically African than the oddly Mediterranean colony back in the south.

All this was reflected in their way of cooking and even the beloved dishes of the Cape took on different accents in the harsher circumstances of a pioneering way of life. Some of this of course has also to be remembered when one considers the food so popular at the Cape in the light of what nowadays would be called its high calory content, its predeliction for sweet things, puddings, pastries, jam three times a day, preserves at elevenses, an elaborate afternoon tea and tea and cake at night. Food, even at the Cape was designed for a more athletic way of life than the refined and increasingly metropolitan society of a highly sophisticated Europe.

Indeed this is just the right moment, at the parting of the ways between the Mediterranean South and African interior, to stress that the disciplines of work and the laws of proportion are just as significant for the proper appreciation of food as the ingredients and the skill of the cook. In fact I think the so-called gourmet, usually a marshmallow in trousers who has not seen the dimples in his pink knees for years as he moves through life by coach, car or train from one elaborate dish to another, is not a true lover of food, but a violator of it. Food of the kind I have described in the physical context of South Africa and the exactions of life which produced it, subject also to the inflexible law of the seasons, was as tasteful and appropriate as any true epicurean could have wished it. This truth can be applied further to the great phase of evolution set off in the kitchen with the arrival of the Europeans in what are now the provinces called the Orange Free State, Transvaal and Natal—the spring-boards for another and equally adventurous leap into what became Southern Rhodesia, Zambia and Malawi. Subsequently it all became linked as well to the German pioneer community settled in South-West Africa on the other side of the Kalahari desert. In the process of opening up these vast areas, contact with Bantu Africa was greater than ever before in the history of southern Africa and it is sad to have to record that even here where Bantu man was safe from slave traders and his societies were far more stable and highly organised, he had almost as little to contribute to the art of cooking as his prototype in the other areas of Africa already trasversed in this survey.

More than ever his was a cattle-owning society and although his women cultivated the land, milk was his most valuable source of food. Cultivation appears to have been concentrated most of all on cereals, particularly millet, which I have so often referred to before in the form known to this day as "kaffir-corn". This the women pounded in mortars carved out of wood which stood on pedestals anything from three to four feet high. Their pestles were like long and heavy cudgels and the sight of a dark African matron, the latest baby tied in a shawl on her back, pounding millet for the daily porridge was a characteristic of predominantly Bantu areas and an authentic symbol of the woman's role in the destiny of African man. Similarly the women of Virgil's Georgics or Homer's Odyssey, singing while they spin the golden flax on their wheel, symbolise the fate of Classical man. Even now, the sound of corn being pounded all day long evokes an acute vision of the whole of Africa before the coming of the European, just as the ardent singing of the turtle and namaqua doves I described way back in the sleeping-sickness country below the Ethiopian escarpment, raise instantly the dawn-fire image of Africa before the coming of man.

The porridge which the Bantu made from millet, as well as his millet beer, which many Europeans still believe to possess healing properties for flagging stomachs and rheumatic joints, were his outstanding contributions to the food of the interior. In fact this porridge, made with skill and with the amenities of a modern kitchen, is a favourite of many Europeans in southern Africa in spite of the introduction of a rival made from the meal of the Indian corn or, to give it its South African name, the mealie.

The pioneers planted mealies wherever they found earth suitable for growing it. Soon it was also as much a Bantu crop as a European one and became a basic feature of Bantu diet as millet had been, so that it is hard to say which of the two sections of the population gained most from the swap.

Breakfast in the best established homes would often offer honoured visitors at least four alternatives for beginning his meal: porridge made either of mealie, millet, or "mabela" oats, or a plateful of cold curds and whey, the historic stand-by of Bantu man all over Africa, but eaten either with sugar or, as we as children did on hot summer mornings, with fresh wholemeal bread crumbled over it and liberal spoonfuls of wild honey added.

Though it is possible to argue over which of the two cereals produces the best of our national porridges, there is no doubt that the mealie was, for a host of other reasons, by far the greater of the two. It is impossible even to whisper the word 'mealie' to South Africans of any colour without evoking the subtlest and most profound associations of childhood and inherited history. This perhaps is best illustrated by its appearance in the most popular of all South African folk-songs. This song was written by a Boer prisoner of war in Ceylon at the beginning of the century. As all good folk-singers do, he sings of all he left behind him in his war-torn native land, in particular of his girl. Each stanza of the song is made infallibly effective as a national tear-jerker by ending the chorus with the line "Down by the mealies and the green-thorn tree where my Sarie [Sarah] lives".

The mealie is integrated into our diet in so many ways and is so much part of pioneering history, not just in the south but all over Africa, that I doubt if more than one per cent of the total population is even aware of the simple fact that we owe it to America and that it is not the primordial native of Africa their emotions assume it to be. Certainly it played perhaps an even greater role in the life of our land than it did in the continent of its origin.

On his march into the interior there was a brief period when the pioneer's attitude to his livestock bore some resemblance to that of the Bantu. They were suddenly too valuable to be used as food except in dire extremities, or rare occasions of exceptional and overwhelming sentimental or communal importance. They were precious seeds of future abundance in the promised land he hoped to find in the interior. As far as possible the pioneers obtained their meat by hunting game which was as abundant in this land as the fish in the seas of the Cape. Out of this hunter's way of life evolved their skill in cooking venison and wild fowl. These skills were to return to the colony of their origin and transform kitchen attitudes there as well. The full round of this evolution took several generations to achieve its consummation, but while on the march the pioneers developed ways of dealing with meat and cereals which even their sophisticated settlements later could not surpass and which remain outstanding features of the national way of eating to this day. For instance, as a people on the move for months and even years on end, they could not afford to linger overnight in camps, waiting on elaborate processes of cooking. They had to rely mostly on substances prepared in bulk during one prolonged stop-over and capable of lasting for months until an opportunity arose for them to be renewed. The incentive or even dynamic in cooking in the land-locked interior was the same as it was originally at the Cape: the search for methods of preparing food so that it could be preserved in the heat and the dust of the long, long journey away from civilisation.

The role that the pickled fish played in the colony of the Cape was duplicated by salted meat, spiced and cured, hanging in strips from ropes suspended between thorn-trees, spreading acacias or wild African willows and poplars that marked some fickle stream, river or natural spring which had been their reason for pitching camp for longer than usual. The Cape Malays called meat cured this way tassals; the pioneering and soon national South African word for it, whether English, Afrikaans, sonorous Zulu or melodious Xhosa was biltong. The English of the towns have always expressed a horror of biltong, regarding it as proof of the cultural barrenness of the interior; a misconception which I can only explain as a manifestation of the irrational urge in all human beings to create for themselves prejudices to sustain illusions of superiority.

I stress this all the more because biltong is just another development of a universal and honoured way of preserving meat or fish which at its best is as delicious as that of the smoked ham civilised man delights in, or indeed smoked salmon. Forms of it are well-known, for instance, in the Americas, for it resembles the carne secca of Mexico and the tassajo of South America, which may have shared, judging by its sound, a common ancestor with the tassal of the Cape Malays. I encountered biltong in the jungles of the Sunda lands of Java during the war where it is called by the Malay name of den-deng. There, the meat of the buffalo, which obviously could not be consumed in a single day and so would rot if not preserved, was cut into strips, rubbed with salt and covered with a coating of fierce chillies and spices to dry it as we dried biltong in South Africa. In fact, during my own time in the jungle behind the Japanese lines in the war, without any source of supplies of my own, I set my troops making den-deng from buffalos I shot and it proved a valuable precaution. Biltong if properly made at home—and it is so easily made, far more easily than curing hams or smoking salmon—is a great delicacy and I am not surprised that in recent years I have come across it increasingly as an *hors d'oeuvres* with pickled gherkins and cucumbers.

The country which comes the nearest to producing an equivalent of biltong is Switzerland where it appears as *Bundtner-fleisch* or, better still, the famous *viande de Grison*. In a country which to my mind serves the traveller today with the best all-round food in Europe—better even than France—this Swiss biltong, delicately carved in ruby red slices, appears without shame on the menus of the best restuarants and hotels.

I believe one of the reasons why the British in South Africa were so prejudiced against biltong was because it usually reached them in an inferior form. Once the country was settled there was no lack of unscrupulous butchers to make biltong out of any wild animal they could shoot in the interior and, worse still, make it out of any part of its meat, however tough or inferior.

The secret of good biltong and the foundations on which its great reputation rests is to make the best out of it meat of no matter what animal is killed for the purpose. At a period when there was no refrigeration and life was constantly one of movement and uncertainty, the game shot for food was never wasted. What had to be eaten fresh was eaten soon after the killing. Parts of the game like liver and kidneys went on a portable grill almost warm from the animal and were considered to be the greatest delicacies. The meat which could be consumed pot-roasted over camp fires and so preserved to be eaten cold for some days afterwards formed only a small proportion of the bulk of animals as large in size as, for instance, buffalo or eland. Indeed, when game of this size was killed, the camp would be pitched for long enough to convert what could not be immediately eaten into biltong. Most of the fat of the animal was cut away and rendered for making invaluable substances like soap or wax for candles. The skins were salted, dried and subsequently tanned to make what we call veld-skoens (veld shoes) or clothes for the men, lashes for whips, bridles, and halters, saddles, harnesses, things for the yokes of oxen, elegant strips for cross-weaving as a base for chairs and beds.

Once the pioneering community could take to permanent farming, the cattle slaughtered for food were dealt with exactly as the game had been and biltong, made out of the best beef, became one of its most prized foods. The meat selected for this purpose was as free as possible of muscle, gristle and sinew. It was cut into solid strips, each weighing anything from three to eight pounds though we found that biltong made from raw meat weighing about six pounds produced the best results. Many South Africans still buy meat in this form to make their own biltong and there is no reason why this example cannot be followed anywhere in the world. Once free of sinew and fat, the strips were first rubbed with a little salt, then left for an hour or so before another good rubbing with a mixture made up in the proportions of half a pound of brown sugar—sugar is a great preservative as well as a disinfectant—to an ounce of saltpetre. It would then be left for a period of anything from one to three days according to the heat and climate in which the animal had been killed, and from time to time rubbed again with the same mixture.

This was, however, merely a basic and in a sense minimum mixture—every household had its preferences in this regard. Some even had to deny themselves the sugar because it was so great a luxury. Yet its presence for delicacy of taste helped to reduce the proportion of the salt, which can spoil biltong for the connoisseur. Others added spices like coriander, nutmeg, basil and even a pinch of ginger. In the interior we were purists in these matters on the whole and were against the addition of more spices than necessary. Some people, mostly at the Cape, later went so far as to submit the meat to marinading in the same way they marinaded their sosaties, and I must admit they made very good biltong this way, although it was obviously a product of a far more settled community than the one of which I am speaking. But once the process chosen had been completed, the meat was hung up in a cool, dry place and left to cure. Done this way, biltong would last for years and though the outside would look hard, dry, unyielding and, to the unaccustomed eye, ugly and unappetising, the inside would still be red, damp, fragrant and delicious. Indeed the meat within could be so fresh that if thinly cut one could grill it or even fry it as a kind of bacon and make delicious supper dishes out of it. One of the great delights we had as children on farms in the interior was to sit on the high plateau, on ice-cold winter nights, huddled close by our open fire, with a dish full of finely sliced beef biltong by our sides. Each one of us would be armed with a little wooden skewer and we would grill the biltong on the wood fire and eat it as if it were some new kind of Arabian delight. Biltong was so tasty and valuable a food in the two Republics the pioneers established in the interior, that it became the subject of legislation, which should be considered in relation to another food that became its closest fellow-traveller. This was none other than our delicate friend, the mosbollietjie of the Cape, grown up into a robust and manly shape and re-baptised as boer-beskuit—farmer's rusks. They were made out of a coarse flour and there were many variations but the following recipe gives an idea of its basic proportions: five pounds of light meal or coarse flour, half a pound of butter or fat, two teacups of sugar, raisin yeast or any other suitable yeast—the trekkers who frequently ran out of raisins made their yeast out of soured dough or, best of all, potatoes —three teaspoons of salt, a pint of milk or, in times of stress, half of milk and a quarter of warm water plus a little extra melted butter. The sugar was dissolved in half the water or milk, the yeast added with about four tablespoons of coarse flour or meal, beaten up well and put aside in a warm place before being mixed with the rest of the flour, salt, sugar and fat to be kneaded with enough of the liquid for a stiff dough. This dough was thoroughly kneaded for at least

three-quarters of an hour, put aside, kept in a warm place overnight, then baked in the oven at a temperature of roughly 370
Fahrenheit. Extracted from the oven, the buns were cut in half and
rebaked into rusks. For long periods on end these rusks took the
place of bread. They proved so valuable that they partnered biltong
as the subject of the legislation I mentioned. This was part of a law
which compelled every male from the age of fourteen to sixty-five
to be prepared at all times to fight for his country. Part of the
preparedness was that he had always to have on hand biltong and
boer-beskuit enough for one month, fifty rounds of ammunition and
two horses. The rusks and biltong were not only chosen because
they were such excellent sustenance, but also because they were
light and easy to carry in saddle bags. I remember even as late as
1914 when we had a civil war in South Africa as a result of the outbreak of the First World War, how my brothers were called up and
what a flurry of cooking and baking there was in the kitchen since
the provision of this law had been overlooked to the extent that
though we had enough biltong we had not enough boer-beskuit to
take them into battle.

Today the baking of mosbollietjies and boere-beskuit is simple
enough but on the march up-country all this had to be done in
ovens improvised out of tins or sometimes cavities scooped out of
the sides of abandoned termite hills which stood like Viking burial
mounds on the veld. None of the people who took part in this
incredible trek into the interior had the time or indeed the facilities
to record their life on the uncharted road. There were one or two
diarists who dealt with important masculine matters but nothing
whatsoever was written about food and these wayside kitchens.

Almost all we know has come down to us, in the same way as the
history of Bantu Africa was transmitted, by word of mouth from
generation to generation. Happily, I well remember my grandmother's eldest daughter—my mother was the youngest—who was
closest to this period. Whenever she came to us on a visit, she would
have to sit up with us night after night trying to satisfy the infinite
curiosity we had as children in this melodramatic period in our
history. As a special treat she would take charge of our kitchen and
cook the things considered delicacies by the pioneers. Things like
the "voortrekker-koekie", a rough descendant of the cookie, which
launched a thousand recipes in our kitchens.

Making bread was a far more serious proposition because of the

longer preparation and greater heat needed at a constant temperature. When there was time and meal enough for bread it was often
done, according to my aunt, in ant heaps. That this was not a story
invented for the delight of us as children, I can vouch for by the fact
that I saw the art demonstrated on my own journeys of exploration
in the bush of central Africa and the Kalahari desert. I had with me
a cook, a man of the Barotse, the great Sutho nation, who have a
kingdom of their own in what is now called Zambia and whose
southern border presses on that most Rider Haggard-like of African
rivers, the Zambezi. He had learned all his cooking from Afrikaner
people who helped the British to establish themselves in the two
Rhodesias. I never knew his age except that he was already getting
old when he came on my first expedition and went blind with
cataract from constant exposure to the sun. He now lives quietly on
a pension thinking over journeys which he will never be able to
make again, as he is so fond of recording whenever I pay my annual
visit of homage to him. He often cooked bread for me in precisely
this way and very good bread it was indeed. But more than bread,
he also cooked for me, exactly as my aunt and our black ladies did,
something I have never found outside South Africa: we call it the
original "as-loek"—ash-cake, or "rooster-koek"—grill-cake, as it is
more commonly called today. This was not a cake at all although it
looked like a much magnified and rough kind of roll. It consisted
of nothing but the dough prepared as for bread, and cooked directly
on the light portable grills every pioneer carried either attached to
the saddle of his horse or in every wagon in his train. In fact, it was
part of the equipment of every farming household of my own day,
and is widely used still.

This cake was directly roasted on red-hot charcoal and when
sufficiently done on one side promptly turned over to be done as
thoroughly on the other. It had to bake very quickly in the first
instance, for it was most important that an all-round crust was
formed instantly to prevent the characteristic damp of the bread
from escaping. When well done and cut open, the dough would not
only be baked in a deliciously dry-damp state but a lovely warm,
fragrant misty smell would rise like incense from the centre. Spread
with butter or even good dripping, salted and peppered, it is one
of the most delicious outdoor forms of bread I know. As far as I am
concerned, whether on a journey of exploration or in the more
sophisticated forms of barbecue like the South African national

institution of braaivleis—no food eaten out of doors achieves its full consummation without rooster-koek. When potatoes, rice and other accompaniments are lacking as they often are out in the bush, it goes extremely well with whatever meat one is able to get. Only one thing is forbidden! And that is to eat it sweetened with jam or syrup as some incorrigible heretics and philistines will do nowadays. Failing all other accompaniments it is good to eat alone, preferably warm from the fire but best of all with a liberal helping of good fresh butter, and a hot and extra-large mug of coffee.

The recipe shows why the rooster-koek figured so prominently on the march up-country as being the best substitute for bread but it must never be thought for a second that any substitute, however good, could ever supplant the profound love and psychological as well as physical need of the pioneer for bread. The pioneers took this love with them from the Cape of Good Hope into the interior. Theirs is the one society I have met on my travels where bread appears to mean to man what it meant in the context of the Old Testament. Bread in my youth was best baked in ovens built out of good red firebricks. These ovens are situated usually not far away from the great loam pots or coppers used for the making of soap which I mentioned earlier on in connexion with moskonfyt. Both were things of wonder to us as children. The loam pots were built into the top of a large square, brick pedestal about four feet high, leaving room enough underneath the pot for a grate in which a fierce fire could be maintained. One of my earliest memories is the vision of one of our coloured maids standing by the copper with a long wooden ladle stirring it as it bubbled and chortled like the witches' cauldron in Macbeth while she sang a strange song over it until the loam for soap was done. Close to it was the bread oven. It was twice as tall and about eight foot long, with a domed roof made of layers of brick laid as closely together as the planking of a boat and in a series of perfect Norman arches. The pioneers clung firmly to the truth inherited from their Dutch and French ancestors that there was no better container for heat than the good red fire-brick—a truth which it amuses me to see is now being applied to the manufacture of electric storage radiators.

Some hours before the dough for the bread had been kneaded and risen sufficiently in the warm kitchen, one of the men would pile the brick oven with dry wood, light it and see to it that the fire never flagged. Whenever he opened the iron gate which sealed the arched entrance of the oven, one looked straight into a world of flame, dancing and leaping in an aspiring and intricate Hindu pattern. I never listened to the story, so often repeated to us as children, of the three who walked un-singed in the Babylonian furnace, without seeing it as a magnified version of our bread oven. To this day it remains for me the archetypal model of the "burning fiery furnace".

By the time the bread was ready for baking, the bricks were heated to their maximum and all that remained of the wood, consumed with all the fury of smoke and glory of flame, were embers, their ruby glow swiftly fading on the floor of the oven. The oven-keeper, armed with a long, fine fire-rake would then see that a bed of charcoal was evenly spread over the floor of the oven. So time-honoured and spontaneous was the co-ordination between kitchen and oven that the moment he finished the loaves would emerge, born aloft, reverently almost, under a canopy of their own light, damp and snow-white blanket like the remains of a distinguished person in some hallowed state cremation. These would be inserted in the oven with infinite solemnity, the iron door clamped to and locked. Although the charcoal within was either dead or dying, the heat contained in the bricks of the oven was enough to produce bread, each loaf with its head high and browned to perfection within anything from one and three-quarter hours to two hours, according to size.

Though bread ovens and loam coppers were, for reasons of safety, usually built in the far corner of the spacious kitchen courtyards, and the air between kitchen and oven would be full of the scents of the wide gardens and vast orchards which lay beyond, the dazzling white walls, the wonderful smell of fresh bread, perhaps after the roasting of meat the oldest cooking smell to give pleasure to the nose of man, would dominate all others as the loaves were carried back triumphantly through the courtyard into the house.

Nowadays, of course, the tendency is more and more to bake bread in the ovens of the latest kitchen ranges. At the time when the best bread was baked in South Africa, our great old-fashioned kitchen ranges had ovens too, large enough for baking bread, but these ovens were reserved exclusively for more finicky and delicate substances like mosbollietjies, cakes, tarts and pastries and I hasten to add, the proliferating race of soetkoekies.

In fact the ovens were never used for roasting even the biggest joints of meat. All meat was pot-roasted and the size of some of our cast-iron pots, used to roast a baron of beef or a leg of mutton, had to be seen to be believed. No appreciation of the nature and particular excellence of the cooking of the interior is possible nor indeed can it be adequately simulated unless the basic principle is accepted that it was assumed, as an eleventh commandment almost, that *all* meat had to be pot-roasted to give of its best.

Another feature of kitchens in the interior was the hood over the range leading up to the chimney. When the fires were out some indefinable instinct would draw us children to peer up the chimney at the clear round of blue sky far beyond. I always thought that nothing in the world could be more beautiful than the light of an African summer afternoon, standing like limpid water in the deep well of the chimney, turning the black soot clinging to its sides into the bluest of velvet. I thought this was a secret of beauty I shared with no other human being in the world. I should have known perhaps that nothing is ever entirely unshared or held alone, because years later when I read Flaubert's *Madame Bovary*, I found that he uses precisely this image of the light of a tranquil afternoon aslant on the soot of a chimney in provincial France to express the peace and innocence of the life of his tragic heroine just before her fall from grace.

At least twice a week we would have a whole rib of sheep, grilled, for breakfast. Nowadays meat is no longer eaten so much for breakfast but done in exactly the same way for dinner instead. We had it twice a week because we slaughtered on an average two sheep a week as the main supply of meat for our large household and numerous servants.

Sheep-rearing, from the moment the pioneers could settle down to permanent farming, became the mainstay of their economy. In crossing the escarpment, which separated the colony at the Cape from the interior, they crossed a land which to the eye looked formidable in the extreme and even by aboriginal standards had a fearsome reputation. It was the part of southern Africa known as the Little and the Great Karoo—a word either of Bushman or Hottentot origin—implying a waterless sort of wasteland. The Little Karoo, more under the influence of the climate of the Cape, had slightly more reliable weather and accordingly was settled first and many features of Cape colonial farming were reproduced.

The Great Karoo which stretched for hundreds of miles beyond the

Orange River into the heart of what became the Orange Free State was the real problem. But by basing themselves first on some rare fountain of water or near a stream, and then slowly spreading outwards, by damming the clefts and depressions of this arid land to catch rain-water when it fell and so securing permanent places of water for their sheep and cattle, the pioneers soon unlocked the secret of this apparently intractable earth. It grew a strange gnarled little shrub with fantastically deep and intricate roots which enabled it to survive long periods of drought. Even on the grimmest of burning days this plant would produce at the end of what looked like a dead twig, a small yet disproportionately thick, green, fragrant and glutinous leaf on which sheep thrived and which gave their meat exceptional flavour.

At an early stage the vital water supply was reinforced by sinking wells and bore-holes. Windmills pumped the water into reservoirs irrigating kitchen gardens and orchards around the first homesteads. This, for me, was always one of the most moving aspects about the pioneers of the interior: although they had rejected the colonial Cape for ever and there was never any thought of turning back, they were pursued by a dream of all that they had left behind. Wherever they went, they reproduced in miniature the gardens and the vineyards which had been the main motive for founding the original settlement at the Cape. As fast as they built homes, they made gardens, planted orchards and ornamental trees. As their water supplies improved they expanded the pattern and were soon sending back to the Cape for greater and more varied supplies of plants and seeds to make each farm a surprisingly green oasis in the wilderness.

The best houses were built on a secure terrace of stone called a "stoep" with the house itself raised in the centre. On the sunny sides of the stoep, particularly the northern and eastern ones, the terraces would often have wooden pillars supporting wooden beams resting inside the walls of the house itself. The beams were inter-trellised with lighter cross-timbers so that vines could be grown, trained upwards and spread across the supporting wood. In the summer one could eat out in the dense vine leaves and by just getting up in due season, pick one's own bunch of grapes overhead for dessert. Since all this apparently arid earth proved exceedingly fertile when it could be watered, these vines reached proportions that were not exceeded even at the Cape. In the orchards too, the peaches and the apricots were bigger, crisper, less woolly and ultimately better subjects for canning and jamming than their prototypes in the colony.

The fig-trees alone were a whole chapter of revelation, so biblical were they in their appearance and abundance. One thought of them instinctively as descendants of the garden from which Adam and Eve were ejected. So automatic was this assumption in our child-like imaginations that we divided our figs into two kinds, each with many a sub-species of its own: the thin-skinned and extremely sweet white varieties were always known as Eve's figs; the large, purple, pear-shaped ones growing into trees so big that we could climb them, were obviously male, and known as Adam's figs. The same process of imagination enfolded the grapes we grew, and there was one kind of grape in particular, which grew in clusters so dense, large and heavy that we called them Canaan grapes because, to the pioneers in the wilderness in search of a promised land of their own, they were like the grapes of which they read in the Old Testament around their camp fires at night; the ones that Joshua's spies, returning across Jordan, had to carry suspended across a wooden stave held by two men, so heavy were they.

Gardens and orchards like those at the Cape were designed to produce something all the year round. In the winter, citrus fruits like the ubiquitous naartjie, oranges and the bitter kind of grapefruit used principally for jam, called pompel-moes—obviously a corruption of the French *pamplemousse*—helped us over the worst part of the period between autumn and summer when no fresh fruit or vegetables were available. Nonetheless there were long periods to be faced without either and despite the fact that supplies of fresh meat and fresh milk were always available, this lack was a hazard to health. It was a world obviously without the benefits of refrigeration. The only means of creating some kind of substitute for fresh fruit and vegetables was by canning or making jam of them. The scale on which this was done in a well-founded household was immense. As a result in my own home in the interior and particularly in that of my grandfather, summer in the kitchen was a period of almost superhuman activity, because quite apart from the exacting daily round of feeding an enormous patriarchal household, the cooks were hard at work making jam and canning vegetables for the long bleak winters. Some idea of the scale on which this happened is evident from the oldest recipes I have found in the archives of southern

Africa. No longer are the proportions stated in terms of cups and tablespoons but often by the bucket or four-gallon tin.

How necessary all this was is perhaps best demonstrated by the fact that when summer came, so starved were our blood-streams of the vitamins necessary for growth in children, that the sudden intake of fresh vegetables and fruit in our diet caused our rejuvenated systems to react so violently against the deprivations of winter that I cannot remember a summer from childhood to adolescence in which all the children in my part of the interior did not suffer from a succession of painful boils. And, hardly had we recovered from these afflictions, when the winter would be once more upon us to start the debilitating process anew. With such necessities to mother invention in canning and preserving, the results were so good that today when refrigeration, the whole technology of mass-canning and the increase of world communication have removed the necessities, people continue to follow the ways of their mothers in these matters for their own excellence.

It is not surprising therefore that vegetables like peas, beans, all the fruit the garden was capable of producing from the smallest plums to the largest peaches were bottled on a massive scale, but nothing compared with the making of jam. Jam was not restricted to a winter role; particularly in the poorer households, it was consumed often three or four times a day, all the year round. Accordingly we must look more closely at the jam or "konfyt" produced in the interior. But first it must be noted that there are some features of the gardens of the interior not found at the Cape.

For some reason the apple which did well at the Cape never thrived in the interior. Its role was taken over by the quince. This I imagine again is something borrowed from the peoples of the Iberian peninsula, where the quince is an honoured product of the garden to this day. But whatever the cause, gardens in the interior grew quinces extensively, often in long dense lanes to provide both fruit and as a defence for the more delicate vegetables against the fierce winds that would sweep across the Highveld.

I remember with joy my gratitude to the quince for ripening as it did in early autumn when all other forms of fruit had vanished and we were already reduced to consuming the grapes we were pathetically trying to preserve against inexorable decline by hanging them up in bunches, each wrapped in its own little bag of white muslin and suspended from the rafters in our driest and coolest attics.

Remembering all this, I am continually amazed at the quince's disappearance from so many modern kitchens and its neglect in the orchards of Western European countries, particularly Britain. The rest of the world has not even got the one inducement people like myself could have for preferring to forget the golden age of the quince because the elastic branches played the role in our young lives that the birch played in that of the young in Victorian Britain. It was both the authoritarian parent's and schoolmaster's favourite weapon for punishment.

One of my first school-rooms was presided over by a fierce old Hollander who always kept not just one but a whole bunch of quince canes in the corner beside the blackboard ready for instant whipping. Quince sticks had many other more creative uses in the economy of the interior, as for example, in weaving the mats on which we cured fruit in the sun, plaiting sheep-hurdles and fruit trellises and acting as a reinforcement within clay walls as iron rods in concrete. Above all they were the weapons used in mock battle among the children of all colours in the land. In this battle two opposing sides sometimes called French and English or Zulu and Amaxosa but in my village and at my instigation, Greeks and Trojans, would draw up for battle. Each one of us was armed with a long quince stick and carried an improvised satchel full of wet, black potter's clay of a gluey constituency. At the first challenge each Trojan would take a lump of clay, press it tightly round the tip of his quince stick, and then, rather like a fisherman casting a rod, whip it at the nearest Greek in such a manner that the clay missile would fly off at right-angles and if the moment was well-judged, hit his opponent smartly but without doing much damage since the clay was soft and pliant.

Quinces were easily made into jam. They were peeled, cored and sliced fairly thickly and placed in either a copper or enamel pot which had been scrupulously cleaned and oiled, and contained just enough water to float the last layer of quinces. They were boiled for half an hour with sugar until the fruit was clear but not mushy. This was one of our favourite jams with bread and butter. Moreover if it had been well made, so that the fruit was still intact in its syrup, it would be extracted and served instead of a jelly with roast venison, particularly a roast leg of springbuck, which is by far the most appetising game to be found in the whole of Africa, as well as with the rare leg of roast lamb or mutton if it was fatter than usual.

Another fruit which appeared at the same time as the quince in the gardens of the interior was the pomegranate, which we have already met as an ingredient of a dish I ate long ago with the Sultan of Zanzibar at the beginning of the East African chapter of this story. It played no great role in our cooking but in the dead period between the disappearance of peach and grape and the birth of a new season with its naartjies and oranges, pomegranate, as a fruit, was an honoured feature of the table.

Properly ripe, each seed extracted and carefully cleaned of its white web and skin, piled up high in a cut glass bowl, moistened with a juice made of sugar and wine, as the French and Italians do for their best strawberries, or just fresh lemon juice sweetened and flavoured with a dash of rum, eaten cold with or without cream, it remains in my memory not only for its visual beauty but as a taste of wonder lifted out of an Arabian Nights entertainment. But the ripeness was all and the moment for picking it could be told when the fruit, gleaming emerald green and gold and shocking pink among its precise and trembling leaves, burst its skin with the wealth of jewelled fruit swollen within and one saw in the cracks through a film as of thin white samite, the ruby light of ripe seeds, mystic, wonderful. Wine glasses or tumblers of freshly squeezed pomegranate juice served cold before breakfast or, for that matter, before dinner were other memorable experiences. The pomegranate, like the quince, could be stored in dry attics and last well into winter.

But perhaps the unique feature of a well-found garden in the interior was the mulberry tree. The mulberry was so much at home in the soil of my part of Africa that it easily out-grew even the spreading chestnut tree under which the blacksmith of the village in Longfellow's poem went to work. Its large, fragrant, dense leaves provided the finest shade in summer of any tree I have ever known. When the mulberries began to appear one's eyes followed them with increasing excitement from a startling phosphorescent green-white shape swelling into a large pillar-box red fruit, finally turning into the most profound purple to show that it was Imperially ripe for eating. These trees by themselves were organic evidence enough of the immense influence which China brought to our culture, particularly the culture of good food, although it was not acknowledged and the contacts which had brought it about had sunk below the horizon of history as taught to us at school. Mulberries grew on such a scale that one tree in the garden of the house where I was born produced more berries than we could possibly use and the whole village was allowed to come and fill their baskets whenever they felt like a mulberry treat. Even so when the leaves fell in the autumn, the earth around the tree itself turned purple from the juice of unpicked fruit crushed and buried in it. An idea of the size that mulberry trees could achieve is perhaps illustrated by the fact that some twenty of us children could play tree-touch in this one tree alone.

We would eat the mulberries raw in the garden or at table on a hot day with cream and sugar. In the kitchens our black ladies would be hard at work making it into a syrup. There was a widespread belief that this syrup, mixed with clear honey, was the best cough mixture for those of us afflicted with sore throats or bronchitis in the cold winter. I have always had a suspicion that the incidence of sore throats and chests in winter up-country would not have been so high among children, if it had not been for the existence of this delicious syrup and the trust of our elders in its medicinal properties!

Well stocked as our orchards were, so great was the need and consumption of jam and other preserves that people in the interior did not hesitate to use what are elsewhere regarded purely as vegetables, as in the case of tomatoes.

This perhaps is the least surprising of all because the tomato is a form of berry and a tomato suitable for jams was encouraged and highly developed in the course of generations in the interior, the two favourite forms being the berry-tomato and the elongated tomato which looked like a model of zeppelins or rugger balls. I suffered so much at school under tomato-jam and its other close fellow-traveller in popularity, pineapple jam, that I can hardly write of it dispassionately. It is many years, too, since I have eaten it but I am assured by many people whose taste I respect that it makes very good jam indeed and it is both original and welcome to people for whom it was not ruined at school.

One reason why I believe the jams of the interior were so good was that the ideal always was to prevent the original fruit from being over-cooked or in the slightest degree mushy. Wherever possible, the fruit was preserved whole or just halved so that the stones which could make some jams unpleasantly bitter, could be removed.

The normal logic of cooking would have made this excursion into the realm of jams and preserves appear at this point an intrusion, but the progression of the history of food in the interior made it imperative that they should be discussed in direct association with the bread for which they were primarily designed and which, after game and biltong, played the greatest supporting role in the food of the interior. This role was so dramatic that old people, in telling us about the trials of their early history, always used one phrase to sum up the periods when they did not have enough to eat. It was a phrase simple enough and yet it filled our hearts with horror. They would merely say: "Daar was dikwels brood gebrek"—there was often lack of bread. To us children, it was the ultimate in deprivation. Nonetheless it must not be forgotten that once the communities became settled and the long dependence on game and wild fowl was over, sheep and cattle could be bred in such quantities that they could be slaughtered liberally for food. Meat could and did become as important if not more important than boer-beskuit, bread, roosterkoek and all the other descendants of this great breed.

First, as I have indicated, came the sheep. The grazing I have mentioned made its meat highly palatable. Normally one ate meat three times a day as many people still do on farms and indeed as they do on sheep-stations in Australia. In the early days mutton was lean because again the facts of life forced even the most docile of sheep to become athletic and there was no problem of dealing with excess fat in cooking. Today when far superior forms of mutton are produced, this is a problem, because mutton fat, unlike that of beef, is more watery and takes far longer to cook than the meat. We solve the problem in our best kitchens in southern Africa by cutting as much of the excess fat as possible from the mutton. We begin our roasting by baking the fat diced or sliced in the pot first, until it is beginning to brown, and then adding the meat. This process produces a kind of mutton crackling which is delicious. But in grilling the whole rib of a sheep without any or with very little fat of its own, the quick process tends to make the lean meat too dry. The fat essential for making the grill truly appetising was found by using the main-gut of the sheep. This may sound alarming to the modern palate, so unaware of the facts of life and the processes which bring their meat to the kitchen, but the main-gut of the sheep thoroughly cleaned and grilled on charcoal until it is dark brown and crisp inside, cut into pieces and served with each helping of rib in the morning, consumed in tiny segments with each forkful of meat, is a truly delicious addition. The rib was always slightly salted and peppered first and usually accompanied kidneys and slices of liver, fried with it on the same charcoal grill, making a kind of mixed grill for breakfast. If preceded by one of the porridges I have described the meat was eaten without any other accompaniment and was followed by bread and butter, eaten preferably with pompelmoes.

It sounds an overwhelming breakfast, but the people who sat down to a meal of this kind came to it usually after some two hours of hard physical work on the farm. They would have been called just before dawn by a servant with cups of hot black coffee or milk with a boer-beskuit or two dunked in it. Before the sun was up they would be out at work letting sheep and cattle out of the kraals in which they had been assembled for protection at night. After getting the work of the day on the farms organised, such a breakfast for us was not an indulgence but a necessity and tasted all the better for being so. It was one of our first lessons in the great truth that a proper appreciation of food, like all good things in life, had to be earned. Sometimes the ribs of sheep would be pickled, sometimes marinaded, both for purposes of preservation and for variation in the routine of the table. And there was another refinement: the meat could be hung in chimneys where only wood gathered from the veld was used. It could be kept suspended there for as long as a week, then washed well, simmered in water until tender and broiled over a charcoal fire.

Leg of mutton was often eaten boiled in the English way, except that we would use very much less water in the process, starting off with only enough to cover one third of the joint in its cast-iron pot, clamping the lid down firmly and letting it simmer slowly for some hours until it was so tender that it would almost fall from the bone. The water would usually be made fragrant with the addition of cloves, some onions and a few carrots and by the time the joint was ready, the liquid would be so much reduced that it formed the basis of a white sour sauce to go with the meat. This sauce was not an imitation of the caper sauce both French and English use with their highly esteemed boiled mutton—mouton à l'Anglaise. It was thickened with as little white roux as possible and soured with lemon juice and grated quince. The joint would normally be eaten with a host of vegetables, and always with both plain boiled rice and fresh boiled potatoes, so that one could hardly ever have enough sauce to accompany it.

The best mutton however was reserved exclusively for roasting. This was the meat of young wethers already running to fat and beginning to bleat as they fed. A leg of a young wether would be treated with the utmost respect. It was usually first given a bath of purification in a mixture of water and vinegar. If necessary it was extensively larded, not just on the surface but with long thin pointed pieces of lard inserted in depth. It would then be studded and spiked with cloves until it resembled a medieval cudgel. Thereafter it would be pot-roasted very slowly and braised until properly brown with a little water or, as times became more sophisticated, with wine. The cloves were easily and quickly scraped with a blunt knife from the dark brown joint when it was done; it would then be borne triumphantly to the table on a large carving dish, surrounded by its own natural sauce. In the Cape they liked to eat a joint of this kind with something sweet and would make a sauce of prunes or peaches stewed in wine. We preferred something that was both tart and sweet and a puree made from some stewed and dried apricots, used in moderation, went well with it—but there was nothing to compare with quince jelly or quince jam.

From early on too we discovered how well beans went with mutton. The formidable law of preserving vegetables to see us through the long, arid winters had very early on taught us to value dried beans and split peas. The dried beans were usually soaked in water overnight and if necessary on into the next day, until needed for the pot. The joint of mutton, without the larding or the cloves, was pot-roasted in the manner I have described. Meanwhile the beans were cooked until just tender and not a moment longer. At the same time a liberal dish of tomatoes and onions was prepared. Both beans and tomatoes were ready about a quarter of an hour before the lamb or mutton. The beans were strained, joined with the tomatoes and both poured into the pot containing the meat. Nowadays it is the fashion to add some red wine to the mixture. Of course this does not actually harm the flavour but to my mind robs the dish of its local character and compels it to drift towards the international standardisation of taste. I prefer the mixture neat, with the cook concentrating on seeing that in the last moments of roasting, the joint is liberally basted with its own fat and the liquid from the mixture of beans and tomatoes, served up finally in a great, deep china dish as hot as a fire-brick itself, and surrounded by enough beans and tomatoes to give a liberal helping to everyone.

The story of the sheep in the life of southern Africa is not complete without something which may be a trifle in substance but nonetheless looms large in the memory of the beginning of cooking there. The first sheep encountered in the Cape was a fat-tailed variety which produced no wool. This sheep was superseded in the national affection by the Rambouillet and other merino breeds, covered with valuable wool, because they filled the farmers' pockets with ready cash; but the fat-tail thrived in the arid regions of southern Africa as it did in the far north and its wethers produced our best meat. For generations it was highly prized and even as a child I thought we were highly ungrateful when the coming of the merino led us to dismiss it with a name of opprobium: "baster-skaap"—in other words implying that it was nothing but a bastard. Yet it was the fat rendered from the tail of this sheep, unusually sweet, compliant and versatile, which figures so prominently in all our earliest recipes. In the long generations on the frontiers before adequate dairy herds were established, it was our "indigenous butter". But in being rendered into fat, this tail produced a by-product which was particularly prized when I was young and which I am glad to say is still found in South African households, particularly South-West African ones in the deep interior. This is the kaiing; a word I believe to be of Hottentot origin because the pastoral Hottentots, on their long march from the north of Africa to the south, brought this sheep with them and were responsible for introducing us to it. The kaiings were produced by dicing the fat from the tail of the sheep and rendering it down into dripping until the cubes became dry, crisp and a deep brown. Since these tails played the same role in the physical economy of the sheep as the hump does in the camel, it was fantastic how much fat they could contain and in real sheep country we always had quantities of these light crisp and succulent pieces of crackling available. They are best eaten hot and obviously are no good for disciplining the waist-lines of the sedentary. But for all that, they are as delicious as they are original and as fitting an end to the story of mutton in southern Africa as they are to the anatomy of the sheep.

Beyond the Karroo which proved itself so unexpectedly kind to the sheep, the pioneers found that the plateau gradually rose higher and the rainfall improved when they reached the great grass-lands of the Highveld of the north. The country became increasingly suitable for rearing cattle and although mutton was never reduced to second place in the kitchen, beef appeared far more often in the diet. In this regard, the cook was faced with several problems. The first was that the cattle were even more muscular and athletic than any of the other animals I have mentioned. This was due, in the first place, to the fact that the whole movement into the interior as well as the system of transport and inter-communication between one town and village and another and above all with the great mother of all, Cape Town, depended on heavy wagons drawn by oxen. For generations the main aim of both Cape colonial frontiersmen and pioneers was to grow the most powerful and hardy breed of oxen possible, so that the life-line with the capital as well as the thrust forward into the interior could be securely maintained, in spite of the lack of roads and the barriers of mountain and river. This aim dominated all others. Milk, butter, the quality of the meat, all were subsidiary considerations.

Another problem was that, away from the towns, an ox or cow produced far more meat than one family could use without grave danger of the meat going bad, however skilled and urgently applied the processes of preservation. The result was that, in the interior, beef for single households was slaughtered only in winter when one could be certain that the meat would not go bad in the days needed for preserving it either as biltong, or in another form which quickly joined biltong in the highest grades of national prestige, the boere-wors—boer sausage.

It is remarkable that the kitchens of the interior should have added a nuance of their own to a food so old as the sausage. One would have thought that by the time they came on the scene all that could possibly be done in ringing changes out of the antique sausage would long since have been done. For instance, the Chinese, a thousand years before the Romans, produced a book on cookery which has a recipe for roasting minced meat in a wrapping of some kind. The Romans had a recipe which commanded the cook to take the breast of quails, the fattest meat of a young lamb, the best meat from the leg of the hare, the lean meat of a pig, mix them together and crush the mixture, how is not specified, but presumably in some kind of mortar, add some honey, salt, garlic, aniseed, coriander, a fistful of bran, stir the lot together, stuff the final mixture into little bags and roast the wrapped meat on charcoal covered with ash. Experts differ about the precise nature of the "little bags" but clearly here was the recipe for a very complex sausage, precursor of the minute little Vienna sausages and Frank-furters as well as giant polonies and haggis. What is even more surprising is that, after so long a tradition, the popularity and quality of the sausage declined so rapidly in the modern kitchen, particularly kitchens of the English-speaking world.

Yet the kind of sausage we call boere-wors has maintained its standing in southern Africa and today is almost the only one of the truly national dishes of the country to have penetrated into first-class hotels and restaurants which, as we have seen, have always ignored local cooking. The quality of the public form of this sausage may have declined in company with the rest of its kin everywhere else, but it is still superior to anything I encounter nowadays in Western Europe, and has lost none of its savour when made in the home. This is due to the fact that it was never made out of scraps of meat not good enough for cooking any other way, nor impoverished mince manufactured out of inferior meat, muscle, gristle and sinew, increased by the addition of stale bread and, I suspect, sometimes even Russian wood pulp, as it is in Britain today.

The original boere-wors, like the original biltong, was made out of the best of the meat which could not be consumed immediately. It must be difficult for modern man in his metropolitan context to realise how much meat there really is on a well-conditioned bullock, let alone a great humped-back ox. Slaughtering an ox raised great problems for cooks and their helpers. When a single beast was slaughtered by us even in my own childhood, with all the amenities of a well-equipped farm and experienced kitchen on hand, a sort of general mobilisation order went out. It would take the entire household working from dawn to sunset before the beef had been properly disposed of: the bones for soup and above all their marrow; such meat as could be used over the next few days as roast joints, steaks or the boiled beef we loved—and this formed only a small part of the beast—were set aside in the coldest larder. All the rest was turned either into biltong or boere-wors. Even the children had a role to play. We would stand armed with needles on either side of the little hand sausage-machines ready to prick the envelopes to release the odd bubble of air which would get caught between the meat and the skin in the stuffing process.

The overall task was made all the harder because one never slaughtered an ox without killing a pig as well. The gut of the pig, scrupulously cleaned in boiling water, was by far the finest envelope for sausage meat. Moreover the lard as well as a small amount of meat, was a vital part of the recipe. Before the arrival of hand mincing-machines, the selected meat was finely carved up on wooden boards with heavy butchers' knives. The man who usually did the slaughtering on farms was inevitably the expert at this. But in my own lifetime this method had already been superceded by small hand-worked mincing machines with a special copper attachment which could be screwed on. The copper "stopper", as we called it, was a largish funnel. The selected pork gut, cleaned and white as snow, was drawn over this funnel until the end nearly touched the point. This end was securely tied up with a strong thread and from then on the force of the mince issuing out of the machine filled the gut and pushed it steadily out on to a wooden board where one of our black ladies, the sleeves of her blue denim blouse rolled up as if for fisticuffs, skilfully helped the filling process along with her supple hands. The sausages formed in this manner looked more like the coils of a garden hose and not at all like the bedraggled chain of elongated meat pulp and bread one sees in butchers' shops in Britain and America. Sausages made in this way were strung across beams in cool, dry, dustproof outhouses, where we also hung our biltong. Most important was the mixing process. Once cured they could be taken on the longest of journeys, cut into slices with a knife and eaten by themselves, far more delicious to my mind than any salami I have ever encountered. But long before they were cured, they could be grilled over charcoal.

In my youth, fresh grilled or roasted boere-wors was a phenomenon which made its first appearance in early autumn and vanished at the first hint of spring. Happily today fresh boere-wors is available all the year round. What is more it is easily made at home because it is no longer necessary to slaughter a whole animal oneself in order to do so. All one has to do is to buy the best beef one can from the butcher, a small amount of the best pork and sufficient thick rashers of bacon to provide the lard and one can make one's own boere-wors to one's own measure, capacity and convenience.

With the appearance of the boere-wors complete in the kitchen, all that was needed for the already mentioned braaivleis was available in southern Africa. Braaivleis is the Afrikaans for the American barbecue, and no doubt its popularity in Southern Africa has been greatly stimulated by the American example. But it is not a mere imitation since it has its own tap root deep in pioneering history. It started, I believe, as an annual commemoration of all that the so-called European in southern Africa owed to the pioneers. The day normally chosen for this was December 16th because on that day, in 1838, some few hundred white pioneers, greatly aided by the extremely gallant Cape-coloured servants who accompanied them into the interior—this part of the story is ignored in our popular histories for political convenience—defeated the armies of the Zulu king Dingaan who had previously and, by all standards, treacherously massacred hundreds of pioneers who had believed they could trust him. To commemorate this year, farmers in the interior would load themselves, their families, bedding and food supplies on one of their heavy covered wagons. Drawn by their best team of oxen they would make for some appointed and usually well-watered place deep in veld or bush to meet some hundreds of other families, pitch camp there as their ancestors had done, often even drawing the wagons into the circular formation used for fighting off enemy attacks, called a laager, and proceed for some days to live life as it was lived on the great march into the interior.

Our own favourite annual meeting place was usually somewhere on the banks of the Orange River, the Great River as it is known among my countrymen. These were extraordinary gatherings—a combination of a prayer-meeting and a political jamboree where official speakers had a field-day. Even as a child I found this aspect of the gatherings boring if not nauseating, but in so far as they were an adventure of living and eating, in wild, natural surroundings, the sort of food I have described, the experience went deep and was incomparable. This type of gathering no longer takes place in the same natural way. Apart from services in local churches, people tend more and more to celebrate the anniversary at home, but the form in which I experienced it was really the basic, the archetypal pattern for the smaller braaivleis, celebrated no longer once a year but almost every weekend in suburban households as well as in the villages and on the farms of the interior.

Every time I return to South Africa I am amazed at the way the braaivleis habit has spread and how even the English-speaking people who have no share in the traditions which gave it birth, have adopted it as a custom of their own. Indeed some of the best braaivleis nights I have attended have been with English friends, perhaps because the chauvenistic aspect which I have mentioned tends to be absent in their concept of the affair and as far as they are concerned it is just an exceptional way of enjoying food in the open air. The food served on these occasions unfortunately is becoming more and more elaborate, side-dishes and wines more and more refined; but I believe that only two things are really essential for a good braaivleis: the original sosatie of the Cape Malays which the pioneers took with them into the interior as a badge of origin or passport for eventual return to the Cape, and boere-wors, the *carte d'identité* of their own in their own world. One can also, without damaging the authenticity of the occasion, enjoy some slices of biltong eaten with a glass of good indigenous dry sherry, or even some of the kaiings I have already described. But when it comes to the main courses I would discard all blatchangs, atchars, sambals and vegetables. I would not have baked potatoes or even bread, but simply rooster-koek. Anything else detracts from the enjoyment of what to my mind is the most perfect combination of food ever devised for eating round a fire in the dark and under the stars in Africa. I would not even serve wine but good hot coffee made as for breakfast. If one must have wine, I would have a wine of the people, sold not in bottles but in kegs. It is honest, straight-forward, up-standing and without any pretence—as I imagine the best of the pioneers to have been. And I would have music, the music which accompanied the pioneers into the interior—the music which is the speciality of the Cape coloured people, played on only three instruments: the concertina, the mouth organ and the guitar. I would not however join in any of the fashionable arguments about the best wood for making the charcoal on which the braaivleis is prepared. There are roughly two schools: that of the Cape which says there is nothing like the dried cuttings of vines or chippings of Cape oak for a barbe-cue, and that of the interior which prefers the shrubs that grow in the hills and have names unpronounceable by English tongues, and in any case need no special mention as they have no equivalents elsewhere. I would simply go as the pioneers did to the driest and best wood nearest at hand to add to my food something of the nature of the earth on which I am privileged to be eating it.

If one must have a sweet at a braaivleis one has, I believe, no choice. It must be pancakes, because pancakes, like waffles, arrived with the first Dutch and followed both Cape-Dutch and French about like their own shadows wherever they went. I would take the oldest and simplest recipe available, the one supplied to Hildagonda by a lady of the good and honoured South African name, Brink.

For these pancakes, the whites and yokes of six eggs are whipped up stiffly, two tablespoons of melted butter stirred into them, as well as half a pound of flour and finally one tea-cup of warm water and a quart of milk. The mixing is continued until a smooth batter without blemish has been formed. I differ from the admirable Mrs. Brink from here on only over the thickness of the pancakes which she says should be that of a crown-piece. At home we preferred them to be as thin and as dry as possible and hence about half the thickness she suggests. Not only is the pancake this way far more palatable but it is also much easier to toss when the moment arrives—an art which is not nearly as difficult as it sounds and which we as schoolboys, armed with stolen materials, learned to practise to a state of expertise and expediency in the hide-outs which we had in our wide school grounds. Normally pancakes made this way were sprinkled with sugar or spread with honey, rolled up and put on a dish in an open oven or close by the fire until we had enough for all to consume; or piled up on a dish with a mixture of sugar and ground cinnamon spread between each pancake and a slice of fresh lemon for each person to squeeze over their portion, according to their individual taste.

This, I would have thought, would have been good enough for any braaivleis, but I once attended one in the garden of friends in Johannesburg which finished with our most sophisticated form of pancake served with a delicious sauce whipped up out of eggs, cream and the national liqueur Van Der Hum.

This mention of Van Der Hum leads me to digress for a moment because it is another national phenomenon that has acquired a certain world fame and now holds a secure place of its own. From the moment the British established a great naval base at Simonstown near Cape Town, it became a favourite with British sailors and they took their taste with them wherever they went in the world. They even drank it the way we drank it, not neat, because it is exceedingly sweet but with a dash of brandy, calling it a Brandy-Hum. In the last war, I served for a time as military advisor to a British Admiral who never ended a meal in his cuddy without offering his guests some Van Der Hum. (Usually, when I was there, he would add: "Have a Van Der Post, because in this ship he makes things Hum".)

How and when Van Der Hum appeared on the South African scene is not precisely known. It has certain similarities with other creamy liqueurs and probably, like most good things in life, is a product of a long process of interchanging influences from many cultures and of many trials and errors. Leipoldt says that he can find no written reference to it before 1850 and adds that the first printed recipe he could discover is the one in the first edition of Hildagonda's book contributed by a Mrs. Cloete, wife of a descendant of the first Free Burgher of the Cape. However, he claims to have a written recipe probably going back as far as 1836 which is almost a replica of Mrs. Cloete's recipe. But, before either Hilda or Mrs. Dykman appeared on the scene, a book of Cape cooking published by a certain Mrs. Hewitt gave a recipe for Van Der Hum which differs only slightly from Mrs. Cloete's. Clearly, in the early days, there were many varieties of Van Der Hum and it is a pity perhaps that this is no longer so. Leipoldt, who claims to have tried all the variations available, says it is impossible to improve on the Cloete formula supported as it is by his own unprinted recipe from 1836.

At a braaivleis in my home province, the Orange Free State, we sometimes end the meal not with pancakes but with a typical melk-tert. The melk-tert in South Africa is not so much a dish as a national institution, almost a fundamental prop of such democratic con-stitution as we have left in the land. It is to us what apple-pie appears to have been and remains to America. It is produced without apology at all hours of the day and night. Wherever one travelled when I was a child, some house on the road would produce the melk-tert it always had ready for any guest who might appear. Every housewife had her own recipe, and would have been insulted if she did not have a fresh melk-tert handy for the most distinguished occasions. In the ample and uncomplicated days before politicians became the demi-gods they are today, one of the greatest of these occasions was the visit by the local priests, or the dominies as ministers of the Dutch Reformed Church are known, so that the melk-tert from early on acquired the nickname of dominie's tert, not to be confused with the more pompous Predikant's tart. No politician who valued his career would risk declining a portion of the melk-tert offered to him during electioneering by the wife of a potential voter any more than he would have dared to refuse kissing their babies. To this day I think that melk-tert carries a grave responsibility for the tendency of politicians in southern Africa to run to fat. However, all these considerations apart, there is no doubt that the melk-tert of the interior is as good a long distance tart, cake or sweet, eaten hot or cold, as a kitchen could produce.

It was made in the proportions of one pint of milk to two table-spoons of sugar, a tablespoon of finest maizina, two eggs, a stick of cinnamon and a tablespoon of butter. The milk was boiled with the sugar and the cinnamon, a roux made of the butter and the maizina and a little milk added, to make it liquid before it was joined by the boiling milk. It was then boiled for about five minutes before being poured into a basin and, when cold, the two eggs, well whisked, were folded into it. It was then poured into a tart dish lined with pastry made as thin as possible and baked for twenty minutes, to be served with a sprinkling of cinnamon and sugar on top. It could be eaten hot or left to cool.

Melk-tert would not be out of place at a braaivleis, but in spite of the trend to the contrary I prefer to end this way of remembering the past and all that food meant to man on his own out in the open and at the beginning of history, by having no sweet of any kind, not even a pancake. Indeed I have often thought that if I had the time to organise a braaivleis of my own, the most I would do in this regard, would be to offer my guests plenty of strong hot coffee to be drunk in the Ethiopian manner with spoonfuls of black wild honey which can still be gathered from the rocks in the hills of the veld and clefts in the gorges made by the Great River near my own farm in the Orange Free State.

It is no longer possible in South Africa to eat game all the year round as the pioneers did—hunting is restricted to the winter months. But there is hardly a farm which has not taken into its protection game of some kind, like the springbok and blesbok and, in some privileged areas, even the eland. Although the vast herds of antelope and flocks of wild birds the pioneers encountered in the beginning are greatly diminished, there are still large areas left in the northern Transvaal, the Rhodesias and south-west Africa where many a household, if it wished, could live in winter on the wild life of the country alone.

Love of game was so all-embracing in my youth that it made the range of such dishes traditional in the Cape seem narrow and highly selective, if not prissy. There was hardly any form of wild life which did not find its way to the table in the interior. I have recipes for instance for cooking the great mountain tortoises found up-country, as well as those of their smaller kin who live either on the veld or have taken happily to living in the water of the dams built by the pioneers. Some of the recipes are for kinds of tortoise bredies, some for ragouts, and soups, one for a tortoise complete in aspic and another for a tortoise cooked in its shell. Everybody who has eaten tortoise recommends it, but I cannot pronounce judgment because in my part of the interior the people believed that the tortoise was sacred and I could never force myself to taste it.

Even the great mountain lizard, the likkewaam, was considered well worth a place on the pioneers' table. Leipoldt recommends it for the fact that it has no "unpleasant after-taste" and "well cooked, is exceedingly tender" and recommends that only the white meat should be used.

Then the various forms of hare were of course a natural for the pot. On a German farm in South-West Africa, where the homestead was built incongruously like a castle in the Rhineland, I once ate a hare-pepper, with home-made pasta or "snysels" as we call our version of it in southern Africa, which would have done honour to any old-fashioned Junker's table. But the hare, good as it is, is only part of the story. The cooking of all the forms of antelope available to my own part of Africa would require a book on its own, seeing that there are some hundred and thirty different varieties. Even the giraffe was highly prized because of its sweet subtly flavoured marrow. Here I cannot speak from experience because by the time I came on the scene, the giraffe was already protected.

The zebra, for all the protection its kinship to the horse tended to give it, did not escape the cook entirely because, suitably marinaded, zebra fillets and steaks cut from good fat animals—it is astonishing how easily the zebra runs to fat—had acquired a reputation for providing the tenderest and tastiest meat of all. Leipoldt, who worked for many years as a doctor in the bushveld where game was and still is abundant, rated zebra meat above that of all other wild animals. Not long before his death he wrote an essay on the subject in which he waxed ecstatic over the recollection of the zebra tournedos he used to bake in the bush. Not even the porcupine, sacred in the stone-age myths of southern Africa, escaped the pot.

The springbok, which has become southern Africa's number one heraldic animal, if not the anthropomorphic totem of the retrogression into an archaic spirit of European tribalism which is in command of the land, is nowadays brought to the table as some kind of ritualistic substance. Yet it could never have achieved this eminence in the imagination of a people if it had not been so lovable and elegant an animal. Certainly it could never have achieved its predominance over all other forms of venison in the kitchen if its meat were not so rare and tender. It not only provided and still provides to this day, the most delicate of biltong, the finest liver, the most delicious tournedos, but above all the most superb natural roast joint available in the whole of Africa. This joint is so highly prized that even in this casual and hurried day there are very few households which will treat its presence in the kitchen lightly.

On arrival in the kitchen the leg of springbok is immediately seized, well rubbed with salt and pepper and, with those who have acquired a taste for the ways of the Cape, a pinch of dry powdered ginger and a very slight scraping of garlic as well. It is then larded like the roast leg of mutton I described earlier on but larded more bountifully, in greater depth and preferably with the lard of bacon that is sweet and unsalted. It is then marinaded and here once again the ways divide in all directions because every household had its own ideas of what constitutes a good marinade. Some prefer a marinade made only out of wine; some, in the remotest interior where wine was inaccessible were often condemned to put it in a marinade of lemon juice, vinegar and water; but in these days of inter-communication, it is generally agreed that a mixed marinade is best.

The larded leg of venison is laid in the marinade for at least twenty-four hours. If it is left too long, the danger is that the meat will lose its texture and tend to become sour because the marinade will penetrate quickly through the incisions made for larding. Care must be taken to see that the leg is turned over every few hours as well as basted with the marinade. It is then ready for baking either in a pan in the oven or, best of all pot-roasting on a lively fire. It is important to let the joint brown well on both sides, in nothing more than its own fat. The moment it is brown, however, a few tablespoons of lard should be added as well as half a cup of red wine, pepper, some cloves and salt to taste. From then on the joint should be put on a lower flame, and allowed to braise gently in its covered pot. From time to time the pot is shaken up so that the sauce flows over the joint. This method is felt to be better than the conventional basting process because the quintessence of good pot-roasting on this scale is to keep the cover sealed, ensuring that no moisture or fragrance escapes from within. It is better that roast springbok should be slightly over-done rather than under-cooked. The sauce which accompanies the meat is the subject of some controversy. Some prefer the natural gravy left in the pan with perhaps a little water added and some corn-meal or maizina used to thicken it, others a more complicated sauce made by the addition of some of the marinade and of their favourite spices.

Among the birds, flamingo was considered the greatest delicacy of all. Again, when I came on the scene the flamingo, happily, was protected. I have never tasted it, but nonetheless it is still brought surreptitiously to some esoteric tables in the remote regions. The indefatigable Leipoldt cannot praise the flamingo too highly but strangely he makes little of the bustard, or wild peacock as the old pioneers called it. I say strangely because all the greatest hunters I have ever known agreed that, properly cooked, it and in particular its kinsman, the gom-pou—gum peacock—were the best of all the large birds. When I tasted it I thought it better than any Christmas turkey.

Guinea fowl, and grouse, wild doves, francolin, wild duck, wild geese, heron, giant stork—none of these birds ultimately escaped the pioneer's pot, except the ostrich, which was used only in the last extremity to provide a kind of inferior biltong. It was altogether a different matter of course when it came to ostrich eggs. In spite of Leipoldt who was ultimately a man of the Cape, I am certain that among the antelope there were two beyond compare and without equal in the appreciation they evoked at any table: the springbok which is nature's equivalent in southern Africa of the sheep, and therefore not surprisingly is found in the parts of the country where sheep do best, and the great purple humped-backed eland, the natural equivalent of beef, again most prevalent in the sort of country where cattle do well.

By the time the pioneers were well established in the interior, the waning influences of the Far East in their cooking were suddenly re-awakened by the arrival of Indians in Natal. They came in their thousands to work on the sugar plantations created in the sub-tropical areas by the British. Their traders quickly penetrated into the remote interior taking their habits of cooking and eating with them. They helped to re-stimulate the flagging appetite for Far Eastern dishes pioneering man had inherited from his earliest begetters at the Cape. Curries again became a regular feature of life in the interior. No week would go by without at least one if not two main curry dishes appearing in the average household. Even such valued orthodox pioneering dishes as "kop en pottjies"—

sheep's head and trotters, and "hoof-kaas"—literally "head-cheese" and the Afrikaans for brawn, were now done in curried forms.

Nothing, as I have stressed, was ever wasted in the pioneering households and no offal was ever considered too mean for the pot. To this day, sheeps' head and trotters and brawn are regular and good homely dishes on South African farms. I have always been grateful for being introduced to them in my childhood if only for the reason that when in the course of the last year I was compelled to *faddel* with my Arab military colleagues I was not as dismayed as the rest of my British fellow officers were when we were presented with the eye of a sheep as one of the greatest delicacies one could have with rice. All that, and more, had been common fare in my youth. In the lowveld in particular not only the head and trotters but also the tripe "pens" of the sheep was served curried all the year round and no survey of food in southern Africa would be complete without pointing to the role offal plays in our kitchens and deserves to maintain in the modern world if only people would take the trouble of preparing them with the care and the love of the pioneers. I have in my youth seen even the head of a slaughtered ox, not discarded, but grilled until it was tender and the distinguished historical gathering for whom it was done in the bush fall on the meat as if it were the best caviare from the Caspian Sea.

The reappearance of curry in the fundamental and most conservative departments of the kitchen of the interior shows to what a depth the Indian influence spread. The best place for curries was and remains Natal. Curry in all the forms in which it is done in India is served in hotels and homes and eaten with relish, however strong the colour prejudice of the household in which they are served. If only the heart in South Africa could be governed for a year or two by the national palate, there would be no apartheid or racial prejudice left in the land, because our cooking is the best advertisement the world could possibly have for a multi-racial society, free of religious, racial and other forms of discrimination, if not even for immediate and inbridled miscegination.

As well as their curries the Indians brought with them mangoes, pawpaws, loquats, and many other oriental fruit that began to appear in the chutneys, pickles and fruit salads of the land. They also brought with them the brinjal, and as they were natural and highly skilled market gardeners they soon made an enormous difference to the eating habits of the country. The brinjal or eggplant, the aubergine of the Far East, became one of the most familiar features of the table, particularly in Natal, whether fried as a vegetable to be served with curries and muttons, or done in a batter and dished up on toast with bacon and egg for breakfast. The paw-paw which is perhaps the most ubiquitous and fast-growing of all sub-tropical fruits, soon appeared in the lowveld of the Transvaal and was used also as a tenderising agent in the preparation of meat.

One custom, inherited from the Huguenots and firmly upheld in the interior was a good soup at night. These were truly soups of stature, because whatever else might fail, there was never a lack of meat and bone to make a good stock. Perhaps the greatest of all was the clear soup made as a by-product of the beef we would have for dinner, boiled, with carrots, onions potatoes and gherkins, clearly a descendant of the *boeuf bouille à la groseille* which is still a weekly stand-by of the peasant in the Midi of France. But it had a close rival in the soup made out of the marrow-bones of the ox. In my own home, largely I expect because Monday was a laundry day, our bread would come out of its burning fiery furnace not at noon but in the evening, so in the winters it had become a family tradition to make this great soup on Mondays. The marrow-bones would be put on to simmer with some onions and carrots just after lunch and by dinner-time the meat and natural jelly clinging to the bone had almost disintegrated into the liquid and readily came away with the soup when it was poured into its great tureen. The moment the soup was poured out and standing safely in the warm, the kitchen would break out into intense activity, for each marrow bone would be extracted and cracked so that the marrow would fall out, yellow, glistening and steaming into the buttered dish placed on the table to receive it. At the same time the cook would take out the fresh baked loaves of wholemeal bread. She would cut the crusts from either ends of the warm loaves so that there were crusts enough for each plate of soup at the table. The crusts were quickly buttered, and the scent of bread provoked by the melting fresh butter as well as the smell of the marrow were among the most exciting I have encountered in any kitchen. Each buttered crust would be piled high with marrow, quickly salted and peppered and the soup and bread be carried triumphantly together into the dining room. As one drank one's soup one ate the warm fresh crust thick with marrow. I cannot recollect ever having experienced a more harmonious, or perfect way of eating anywhere else in the world.

I never go back to South-West Africa without feeling, despite the aeroplane and the motor-car, that I have gone back also in time to the sort of community I knew as a child. Perhaps all this is best summed up in an experience I had there several years ago. I was on a journey from Windhoek to the Etosha Pan in the far north. I had set out before dawn and when the sun rose was not yet in sight of any town. I asked my driver how long it would take before we would get to a town.

He answered with another question: "Are you hungry?" "Yes", I said, not troubling to explain that I was more thirsty than hungry. "Well, why wait for the town" he said, turning off the main road along a track as he spoke "when there is such a clear koffie-paaitjie" right here?—the last term means literally a "little coffee road."

I recollected with a rush of warm emotion that when I was young that was precisely what we called any road which indicated that some form of human habitation might be near where one would be warmly welcomed with coffee, food and shelter.

The custom has declined almost to vanishing point in my own part of Africa and to find it taken for granted there in the south-west was as surprising as it was reassuring. I did not protest but allowed him to follow the road. It brought us, after some miles, to the homestead of a farm rearing karakul, the black-nosed sheep that produces astrakan fur. It was owned by a family of German origin and the welcome could not have been more generous and more traditional than the name koffie-paaitjie implied.

I not only had coffee but sat down to a breakfast of porridge made out of mealie-meal, served with cream and honey. It was followed by bread and a scrambled ostrich egg. This was another coincidence to heighten my illusion of having re-captured the vanished past in which these eggs played such a role.

I was still thinking of it at dawn the next morning when I said goodbye to my generous host. The morning star was already high in the eastern sky over the Kalahari—the star which plays such a heroic role in the stone-age mythology of my native country under the name of "The Dawn's Heart". Watching it, I suddenly realised why the ostrich egg had so completely captured my imagination. The ostrich has a very special role in the early mythology. It is the bird which inadvertently brought the gift of fire to man and was punished for doing so by having its power to fly taken away from it.

The bird, in the symbolism of many men, is the image of inspired thought. For this reason Plato compared the mind of man to a cage of birds. It is clear why the ostrich was chosen for its Promethian role; fire was the most inspired and greatest of all ideas ever to issue from the mind of man and only the greatest bird of all, the ostrich, could adequately symbolise it. I realised suddenly why on the last day of all of my many expeditions to the same Kalahari over which the day was just then breaking, I had always pitched camp near one of the many dead trees which stand upright like ghosts in the desert. At night I would make a fire around it and eat my last meal watching the fire climb up the dead wood until finally it stood there like an immense Gothic cathedral of flame in the dark. I would watch it, feeling intensely grateful and moved for the gift of fire, moved above all, I remembered now, because among the many good and great things fire did for man was to release him from the bondage of having to eat his food raw. It made him free to set out on the long road towards evolving an art of cooking which is one of the highest expressions of culture and civilisation, because it converts food from a mere necessity into a source of delight and a cause for rejoicing in being alive, however cold the day or dark the night.

Index

213